Marine Med
Dies

by Dr Denis Griffiths
BEng (Hons), MSc, PhD, CEng, FIMarEST

Sponsored by
ExxonMobil
Marine Lubricants

Published by IMarEST
The Institute of Marine Engineering, Science and Technology
80 Coleman Street ● London ● EC2R 5BJ

www.imarest.org

A charity registered in England and Wales
Registered Number 212992

First published in 1999 by The Institute of Marine Engineers (Now IMarEST)
This reprint 2004

ISBN 1-902536-18-5 paperback

British Library Cataloguing-in-Publication Data
A catalogue record for this book is available from the British Library

Contents

Acknowledgements		i
1	**The Medium Speed Diesel Engine**	**1**
1.1	Compression Ignition Engine	1
1.2	Trunk Piston Arrangements	2
1.3	Engine Cycles	3
2	**Engine Construction**	**10**
2.1	Engine Structure	10
2.2	Connecting Rods	17
2.3	Pistons And Piston Rings	22
2.4	Cylinder Liners	34
2.5	Cylinder Head	40
2.6	Camshaft, Cams And Valve Operating Mechanisms	50
2.7	Engine Governor	65
2.8	Turbocharger Systems	73
2.9	Engine Drive Pumps And Coolers	81
3	**Engine Choice and Installation**	**89**
4	**Operation**	**103**
5	**Operational Support Systems and Performance Monitoring**	**110**
6	**Maintenance**	**118**
6.1	The Crankcase	123
Index		137

For Peter H. Gee and Fred M. Walker.
Two very good friends.

Acknowledgements

The author would like to thank Wärtsilä NSD Ltd, MAN/B&W and the Woodward Governor Company for help with information regarding the equipment they manufacture. The author also wishes to express his gratitude to Mike Wilson and David T. Brown in particular for their assistance with specific problems and for their enthusiasm for the project. Thanks are also due to Members of the Book Advisory Committee of the Institute of Marine Engineers, without their efforts no books would be published by the Institute.

1   The Medium Speed Diesel Engine

Medium Speed Engine Classification

The classification of the marine medium speed engine is broad, encompassing a wide range of operating speeds, two operating principles and propulsion and electrical power generation applications. The broad classification means that it is difficult to define and no book can give comprehensive coverage, at least within a reasonable sized volume. This book is intended only as a guide, and reference should be made to operational manuals for individual engines before any action is taken.

Definition of Medium Speed

A medium speed engine can be considered as one operating within the normal speed range of 200 rev/min – 1000 rev/min. For propulsion purposes the shaft speed must generally be reduced by gearing or through the adoption of a diesel-electric drive, to obtain the most efficient propeller speed. When employed as a prime mover for electrical generation purposes the engine operating speed is chosen, in conjunction with the design of the electrical equipment, to give the desired power supply frequency. Aboard ship a frequency of 60Hz is usual, therefore the engine speed and electrical equipment arrangement must be capable of producing this.

1.1   COMPRESSION IGNITION ENGINE

A diesel engine is a compression ignition engine and this means that the air charge in the cylinder must be compressed to a high enough temperature to ensure that the fuel will ignite spontaneously when injected into the cylinder. The compression ratio is chosen to achieve the desired air temperature in the cylinder at the end of compression.

The governing equations are:

Equation 1:

$$\frac{P_1 V_1}{T_1} = \frac{P_2 V_2}{T_2}$$

Equation 2:

$$P_1 V_1^{\gamma} = P_2 V_2^{\gamma}$$

They can be combined to give equation 3:

$$T_2 = T_1 \left(\frac{V_1}{V_2}\right)^{\gamma - 1}$$

Where:

P_1 = the initial cylinder pressure.

V_1 = the initial cylinder volume.

T_1 = the initial air temperature.

P_2 = the final cylinder pressure.

V_2 = the final cylinder volume.

T_2 = the final air temperature.

γ = the index of air compression.

It can be seen from equation 3 that the final temperature T_2 depends upon the initial temperature of the air in the cylinder as well as on the compression ratio V_1/V_2. Any reduction in initial air temperature will reduce the final air temperature but any leakage of air from the cylinder will also reduce the final temperature, which could influence fuel ignition.

1.2   TRUNK PISTON ARRANGEMENTS

Although over the years many different designs of medium speed engine have evolved the most common type at the time of writing is the trunk piston arrangement. This form provides a low engine height, favoured by shipowners due to the headroom saving compared with the tall crosshead engine. Trunk engines have cylinder liners which open directly into the crankcase so that products of combustion and unburnt fuel pass directly from the cylinder into the crankcase causing contamination of the lubricating oil; however, given that no more satisfactory arrangement exists, the trunk piston arrangement is the best option available. A connecting rod provides the drive from the piston directly to the crankshaft and the angularity of the connecting rod means that there is a side thrust from the piston to the cylinder liner. The magnitude and direction depend on the force on the piston and the direction in which the piston travels, up or down the cylinder. This side thrust can increase cylinder wear (see Figure 1).

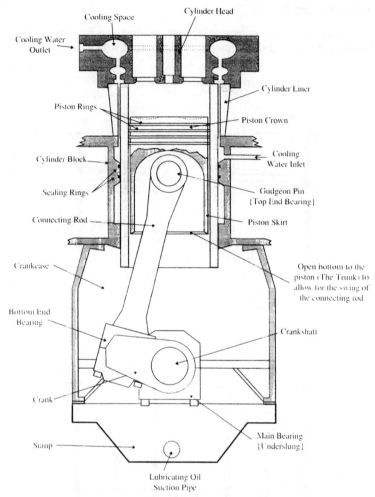

Figure 1. General Arrangement of a Trunk Piston Heading

1.3 ENGINE CYCLES

Medium speed engines may operate on the four stroke cycle or the two stroke cycle. Although the former is favoured by most marine engine builders a number of two stroke medium speed engines are still in service. The fundamental structure of both types is similar and the combustion process is the same, the basic difference is in the gas exchange process.

Four Stroke Cycle

The four stroke cycle engine has four distinct piston strokes or two revolutions of the crankshaft for each power output stroke **(Figure 2)**.

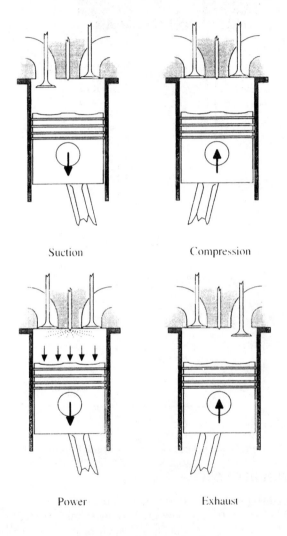

Suction   Compression

Power   Exhaust

Figure 2. The Four Stroke Cycle

a. During the suction stroke the piston moves down and air is drawn into the cylinder through the air inlet valve(s).

b. During the compression stroke all valves are closed so the piston moves up.

c. Near the top of the stroke the fuel injector opens and sprays a quantity of fuel into the cylinder. This ignites quickly if the temperature is correct, producing a rapid rise in pressure which causes the piston to move down the cylinder. Power is transferred to the crankshaft via the connecting rod.

d. During the exhaust stroke the piston is moved upwards by the crankshaft and the products of combustion – the exhaust gases – are forced out of the cylinder through the exhaust valve(s).

It can be seen that power is produced only during one of the piston strokes during the four stroke cycle **(Figure 3)**.

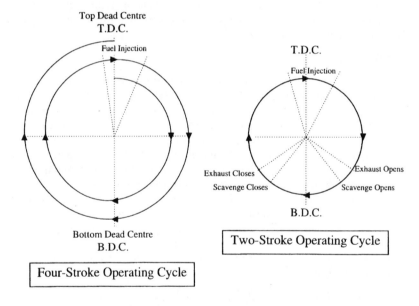

Figure 3. The Four Stroke and Two Stroke Operating Cycles

Two Stroke Cycle

The two stroke cycle has one power stroke of the piston for each crankshaft revolution. There are no distinct exhaust and air suction strokes and so provision must be made for the removal of the exhaust gas from the cylinder before it is recharged with fresh combustion air. This process is known as

5

'scavenging' and involves the incoming charge air forcing out the exhaust gas through ports cut in the cylinder liner or valves in the cylinder cover. An essential feature of the two stroke cycle engine is that combustion air must be provided at a pressure above that of the atmosphere to ensure that exhaust gas will be forced from the cylinder by the incoming scavenged air. Such air can be supplied by crankshaft driven pumps or chain driven rotary blowers, but most engines employ exhaust gas driven turbochargers. An air trunking, generally known as the scavenge air manifold, runs the length of the engine and surrounds the scavenge air ports. Air is supplied to the cylinders through ports cut in the lower part of the liner. This means that the pistons of two stroke cycle engines must be provided with long skirts to ensure that the ports remain covered when the piston is at the top of its stroke. If this was not so there would be a loss of air into the crankcase and, in the case of an engine with exhaust ports, blowback from the exhaust into the crankcase and scavenge manifold with its associated problems, including the risk of explosion. Such two stroke cycle engine pistons require sets of sealing rings at the lower part of the skirt **(Figure 4)**.

Port Scavenging

For a port controlled two stroke cycle engine there are exhaust and scavenge air ports cut in opposite sides of the lower part of the cylinder liner. As the piston moves downwards during the power stroke it will uncover the exhaust ports and the cylinder pressure will fall to a value below that of the scavenge air pressure by the time the piston uncovers the scavenge ports. The piston crown is profiled to encourage the incoming air to flow upwards and so effectively remove all exhaust gas from the cylinder, which is known as cross flow scavenging. On the upward or compression stroke of the piston the scavenge ports are covered before the exhaust ports and some air is lost from the cylinder. However, the designer will have allowed for this and there will still be sufficient air in the cylinder for efficient combustion provided the scavenge air supply pressure is at the design value. The area of scavenge and exhaust ports is crucial to effective engine operation and it is essential that these ports be kept clear of carbon deposits.

Uniflow Scavenging

In some cases one or more exhaust valves in the cylinder cover are used to control cylinder exhaust, the opening and closing of such a valve being regulated by a camshaft. The exhaust valve will open before the piston uncovers the scavenge air ports in the lower part of the liner, allowing the cylinder pressure to fall below the scavenge air pressure. When the scavenge ports are uncovered, air flows upwards and forces the remaining exhaust gas from the cylinder. This is known as uniflow scavenging.

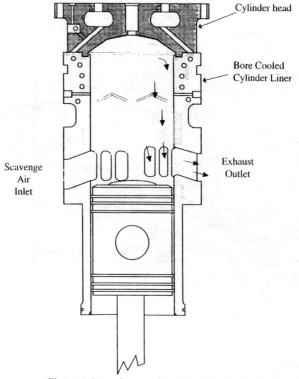

Cylinder head

Bore Cooled
Cylinder Liner

Exhaust
Outlet

Scavenge
Air
Inlet

Figure 4. Loop Scavenging - Two Stroke Cycle

In-Line and Vee Arrangements

Medium speed engines may be of the 'in-line' or 'Vee' type. As the name suggests in-line engines have their cylinders arranged in a single line while the Vee type engine has two banks of cylinders, arranged in Vee form, but only a single crankshaft. For approximately the same length of engine the Vee form has twice as many cylinders as the in-line form and can generate twice the power. Cylinders are generally angled at about 45° to each other and opposite pairs of cylinders are connected to the same crank. Each cylinder will have its own operating gear, in the form of valves, fuel pumps, cams, etc., but there is a saving in terms of the crankshaft, main bearings and engine structure. A Vee form engine will occupy less engine room floor space compared with two in-line engines of the same total power, and will also have a lower height. Depending on individual engine design, certain parts of Vee form engines may be less accessible than their equivalents on in-line engines, and maintenance can be more complex **(Figure 5)**.

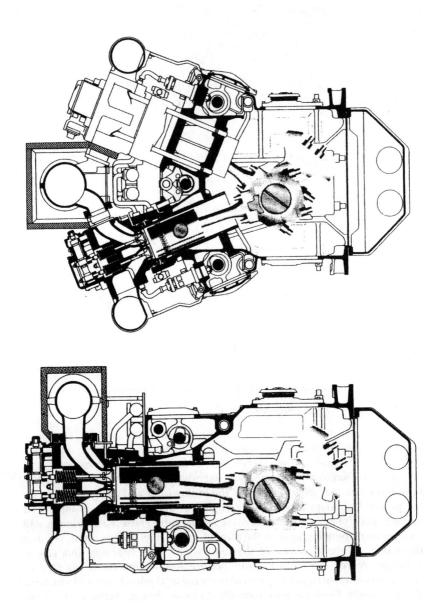

Figure 5. Sections Through In-Line and Vee Type Engines

Summary of the Medium Speed Diesel Engine

Diesel engine: Compression ignition engine and need for high air temperature in order to ignite the fuel when injected.

Engine operating cycles: Two and four stroke operating cycles described.

Engine arrangements: In-line and Vee type described.

2 Engine Construction

2.1 ENGINE STRUCTURE

Traditional Engine Structure

A traditional engine structure arrangement comprises a cylinder block which accommodates the cylinder liners; the block differs in design depending on whether the engine is of in-line or Vee form. The block has spaces to accommodate camshaft drive arrangements (chain or gear), a housing for the camshaft and doors allowing access to the crankcase. The block is a single casting to ensure rigidity. Cast iron is the usual material. Supporting the cylinder block is the bedplate with its main bearing housings and mounting feet, which connect to the ship's structure. In some cases tie rods are employed to maintain the main bearing housings and engine block in compression; the steel tie rods pass from the upper part of the cylinder block to the lower face of the bedplate below the main bearing housing. Smaller engines often have no tie rods as the structural section thickness is great enough to keep tensile stresses reasonable during peak pressure periods. With a casting there is a minimum section thickness requirement to ensure that the molten metal flows readily to all parts and this thickness is often greater than that dictated by actual stress considerations. Accurate alignment between bedplate and cylinder block is essential to effective stress transmission and engine operation.

Modern Cast Monoblock Structure

Engines designed during the 1990s generally employ a cast monoblock form of construction with the cylinder block and bedplate forming a single cast iron structure. This nodular iron casting provides considerable rigidity due to its single-piece design and construction. In some engines additional strengthening can be provided by long tie rods extending from the lower face of the main bearing to the upper part of the structure. Tie rods are also employed between the upper face of the cylinder head and the lower face of the intermediate frame structure to ensure that combustion loads are transmitted from the cylinder head to the engine frame structure. The use of tie rods does not imply a weakness in design and is an effective use of a strengthening mechanism where it is needed. A rigid structure is necessary in order to preserve alignment of all engine parts, particularly the crankshaft and camshaft, and to minimise problems related to vibration of the structure. Some engines (e.g. Wärtsilä Vasa 38) have the air inlet manifold as an integrated part of the engine block while many water and oil channels are cast-in or machined as part of the engine structure. Such features make for easier maintenance, improved accessibility and a reduction in the number of engine parts **(Figure 6)**.

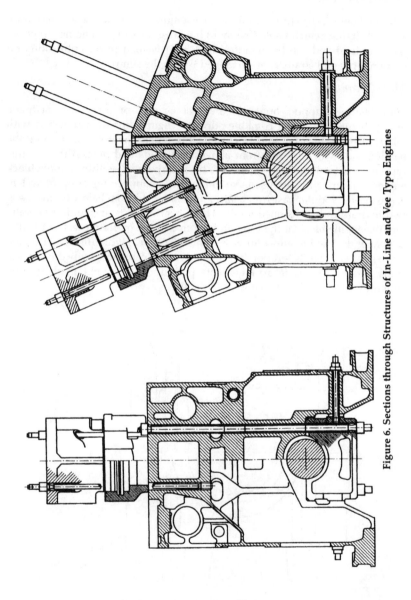

Figure 6. Sections through Structures of In-Line and Vee Type Engines

Engine Sub-Frame

With monoblock structures, a sub-frame is required to act as the engine sump. This sub-frame, which bolts directly to the lower face of the engine structure, takes no load and can be manufactured from welded plate. Lubricating oil suction pipes and strainers are arranged within the sump.

Main Bearings

Main bearing support housings are cast as part of traditional bedplate arrangements, and these combine adequate rigidity for the crankshaft with relative ease of bearing adjustment. Bearing replacement requires lifting the bearing cap, which is held from above with studs and nuts. Although this type of arrangement can, in theory, be incorporated within a monoblock engine structure, it is not used. An underslung main bearing support system is preferred. Nodular cast-iron bearing caps are held from below by means of two hydraulically tensioned studs. These bearing caps are guided laterally into the engine block at the top and bottom and the hydraulic jacks are often permanently fitted to allow for ease of maintenance. Hydraulically tensioned horizontal side studs support the main bearing caps and with the vertical studs and lateral guide arrangements provide a very rigid main bearing support for the crankshaft **(Figures 7 and 8)**.

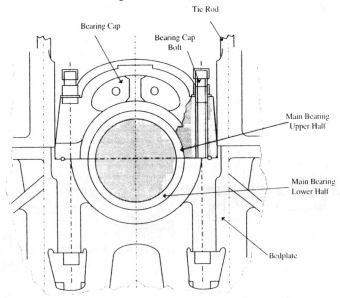

Figure 7. Main Bearing Arrangement

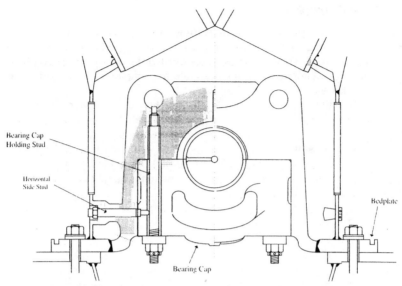

Bearing Cap
Holding Stud

Horizontal
Side Stud

Bedplate

Bearing Cap

Figure 8. Main Bearing Arrangement for Underslung Crankshaft

Crankshaft and Main Bearings

Crankshafts for medium speed engines are solid forgings from a single alloy steel ingot. Solid forging avoids stress problems, which would result from the presence of shrink fits, and ensures even stress transmission between journals, webs and pins. There are very rigorous Classification Society rules governing the dimensioning of crankshafts, based on a combination of theory and experience. Current designs make considerable use of computer finite element analysis which allows a wide range of loadings, dimensions and cylinder firing orders to be analysed before any manufacture takes place.

Crankshaft Arrangements

A crankshaft must be able to transmit the torque developed during operation. This torque imposes stresses on the crankshaft journals. Pins are subject to direct stresses from the connecting rods, which impose bending and shear stresses. Webs bend due to this loading but they also have a tendency to twist. Crankshafts will bend under load as each cylinder unit section acts like a simply supported beam, with the main bearings acting as the supports. Loadings vary with time making the analysis of stresses a complex matter, further complicated by the presence of oil holes through journals, webs and pins.

Crankshaft Loadings

To support the loadings applied, all bearings should be as large as possible, to keep the oil film stress within acceptable limits. Increasing the length of journals and pins tends to increase engine length, which is unacceptable. Instead, large diameter pins and journals are employed to provide large bearing surface areas. Use of thin webs allows for longer pins and journals while still maintaining a reasonable distance between cylinder centres. The throw of the cranks is governed by the selected piston stroke (crank throw is half the length of stroke) but through the use of large diameter pins and journals it is possible to obtain overlap between the journals and crankpin, increasing the rigidity of the shaft and limiting its tendency to bend when under load. This overlap also increases the torsional rigidity of the crankshaft and reduces torsional stress **(Figure 9)**.

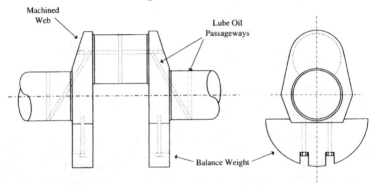

Figure 9. Section of Crankshaft

Crankshaft Balance

The firing order of an engine is primarily chosen to reduce engine torque fluctuations and minimise vibration. Any final solution must be something of a compromise as other factors have to be considered including exhaust arrangements, bending loads on the crankshaft and torsional vibration. Reciprocating masses – the pistons, connecting rods, webs and crankpins – induce vertical forces which can result in vibration. Reducing the mass of these components through the use of lighter materials and removal of all unnecessary materials will help to minimise vibration but will not eliminate the problem. Most medium speed engine crankshafts are machined all over in order to reduce excess weight. They are provided with adequate fillets at all changes of section in order to avoid stress raisers which could give rise to fatigue. Changes in section occur between journal and webs, crankpins and webs, and at oil holes. In many cases balance weights are fitted to some or all of the webs; these are designed to oppose the vibration induced by the reciprocating masses. The solution is only partial as a rotary mass will not only induce vertical forces to oppose the reciprocating masses but it will also induce variable sideways forces, causing transverse vibration. The size and positioning of balance weights are carefully arranged by the designer and should not be changed.

Torsional Arrangements

Torsional vibration must be minimised as far as possible, as it induces stress which can give rise to fatigue failure. Although the designer can take steps to reduce torsionally induced stress, it cannot be eliminated, and many engines are fitted with torsional vibration dampers at the free end of the crankshaft (the end opposite to the flywheel). The torsional vibration damper acts to reduce the amplitude of vibration, lowering the induced stress intensity. Engine driven pumps for lubricating oils and cooling water circulation are also usually fitted at this end of the crankshaft. For larger engines the flywheel is generally toothed, allowing a turning motor to be connected.

Thin Shell Bearings

Main bearings for medium speed engines currently in use are of the thin shell type. Similar bearing shells are employed for bottom end bearings. This type of bearing essentially consists of a thin steel backing shell with a layer, or layers, of bearing material cast, flashed or deposited on the rubbing surface. This type of bearing is prefinished and does not require scraping to fit; indeed no scraping is possible due to the thin layer of bearing material present. Over the years bearing materials have changed to meet the operating conditions. Early arrangements simply had a layer of white metal on the steel backing shell but this gave way to the multi-layer bearing with a layer of lead-bronze or copper between the steel and white metal in order to improve adhesion. This layer also provided an emergency bearing surface. The use of overlay material provides a degree of protection against corrosion, while a thin layer of nickel prevents the lead in the overlay from migrating into the lead-bronze layer. The backs of the steel shells may have a soft layer which is designed to prevent corrosion. During the 1990s a number of engine builders returned to bi-metal bearings which employ a layer of aluminium-tin on the steel backing shell. Others employ a multiple layer bearing with a tin-antimony rubbing surface over a copper-lead layer on the steel backing shell. Bearing technology continues to change to meet the demands of higher loads but problems of lubricants contaminated by water and residual fuels must also be overcome **(Figure 10)**.

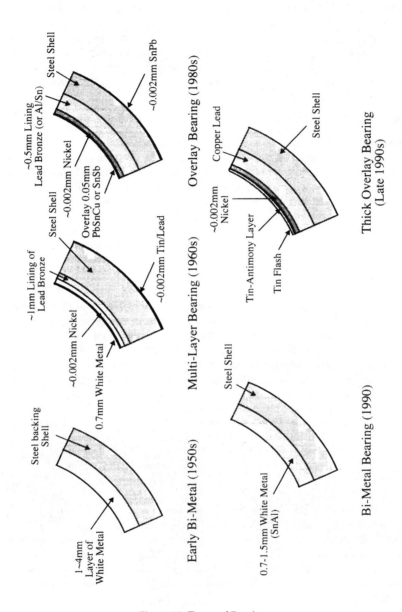

Figure 10. Types of Bearing

Bearing Shell Fitting

Bearing shells must provide an even bearing surface when they are in position and the bore of the housing must be accurately machined. Shells are slightly larger than the bore so that when the housing is tightened the 'nip' ensures the bearing has the correct shape and bore. Engines used for propulsion via a gear-box will be provided with a thrust bearing somewhere in the shaft system. This will take the thrust from the propeller and also take thrusts resulting from the pitching of the ship. For electrical generating prime movers a separate thrust is sometimes not provided, so there should be some internal arrangement for axially locating the crankshaft. This is usually accomplished by providing rubbing strips on the edges of one set of the main bearing shells. These rubbing edges act like thrust bearings and mate with a flange or crank web on each side of the main bearing. The Sulzer ZA40S engine has a thrust bearing fitted at the main bearing next to the flywheel, this bearing being fitted on the outside of the engine casing.

Bearing Shell Removal

With underslung crankshafts the upper shell can be easily removed from the housing as the weight of the running gear is not on it. Bedplate mounted crankshafts have the weight of the crankshaft and running gear on the lower shell, therefore the shaft must be raised slightly in order to remove that shell.

2.2   CONNECTING RODS

Connecting Rod Design

Connecting rods are forged from alloy steel and machined all over. The basic connecting rod requires a provision for attaching it to the crankpin, at the bottom or large end bearing, and to the piston at the gudgeon pin, the top or small end bearing. The small end generally consists of a bush inserted in a hole bored in the top of the connecting rod. The bush may be a simple bronze affair but some engines, particularly a high powered unit, have white metal lined, or tri-metal, bushes. Lubrication for the top end bearing comes from the crankshaft via the bottom end and a hole drilled in the connecting rod. This passageway is also used to conduct cooling oil to the piston. Because of the high loadings on the small end bearings and the absence of complete rotary motion, an adequate supply of lubricant is essential at all times. Stepped small end bearings are used to provide a large bearing surface on which the piston force may act via the gudgeon pin **(Figure 11)**.

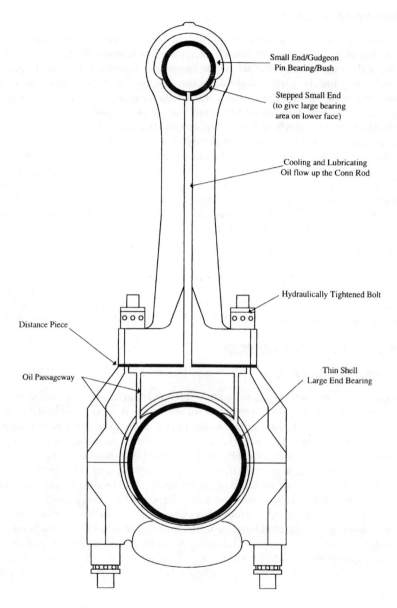

Small End/Gudgeon
Pin Bearing/Bush

Stepped Small End
(to give large bearing
area on lower face)

Cooling and Lubricating
Oil flow up the Conn Rod

Hydraulically Tightened Bolt

Distance Piece

Oil Passageway

Thin Shell
Large End Bearing

Figure 11. Connecting Rod Arrangement Showing Oil Pathway

Large End Bearing

The large end bearing can present certain maintenance problems. The traditional fixed centre connecting rod has the upper part of the large end housing forged as part of the rod, which means that the lower part of the connecting rod is wide in order to accommodate the bearing shell and securing bolts. In order to remove the piston, with the connecting rod still attached, the bottom part of the connecting rod must be no wider than the cylinder bore through which it will be lifted. Modern engines employ large diameter crank pins in order to provide large area bearings and low bearing loads. A fixed centre connecting rod design would not be suitable. Alternative arrangements are available.

a.   A small palm may be fitted to the foot of the connecting rod which in turn attaches to a conventional marine type large end bearing. The small palm end can pass up the cylinder liner but there is a large end bearing of sufficient diameter. The provision of shims at the palm end allows adjustment of the compression ratio while the shorter section of connecting rod allows a lower piston withdrawal height **(Figure 12)**.

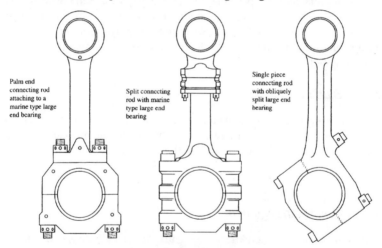

Palm end connecting rod attaching to a marine type large end bearing

Split connecting rod with marine type large end bearing

Single piece connecting rod with obliquely split large end bearing

Figure 12. Connecting Rod Arrangements

b.   The connecting rod may be split, with a palm connection between the upper and lower sections. The palm end joint can be disconnected allowing the piston to be removed while the large end and lower part of the connecting rod remain on the crankpin. This arrangement allows a very small piston withdrawal height and enables the compression ratio to be adjusted, if required, by using shims at the palm connection.

c. An obliquely split large end allows the two parts of the large end to be separated. Because of the oblique split the piston and its connecting rod may be drawn up through the cylinder liner. The two parts of such a large end arrangement are usually serrated at their mating faces to accommodate shear stresses.

Bearing shells for large end bearings are similar to main bearing shells but are provided with large oil holes in a central channel. These allow oil to flow from holes in the crankpin, through the bearing, to passageways in the large end and then up the hole in the connecting rod. Tags, or similar, on the bearing halves mate with location points in the housings to ensure correct alignment. As with main bearings the thin shells rely on the accuracy of the bore machined in the large end to preserve a true circular shape. Correct tightening of the large end bolts is, therefore, essential.

Vee Engine Large End Arrangements

Vee form engines require special large end bearing arrangements as there are two pistons connected to each crankpin. The small end of the connecting rods will be similar to the bushed small ends employed for connecting rods of in-line engines, but there are three different ways in which the large ends can be designed.

Side-By-Side Positioning

Side-by-side positioning of large end bearings on the crankpin is probably the simplest and most popular design, as each connecting rod can be treated completely separately. This requires the centres of the two cylinders connected to each crank to be slightly out of line across the engine, unless the connecting rods are bent, so the engine length will be slightly increased.

Fork and Blade Arrangement

A fork and blade arrangement of large ends allows cylinder centres to be in line across the engine. It does mean that one connecting rod large end must be divided into two (the fork). The other connecting rod large end (the blade) is accommodated in the fork opening. There are two possible designs for the bearings (see Figure 13).

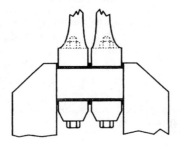

Side by Side Arrangement

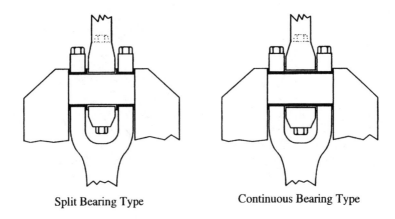

Split Bearing Type   Continuous Bearing Type

Fork and Blade Arrangement

Figure 13. Bottom End Arrangements for Vee Type Engines

a. The fork may have two short large end bearings. The blade large end will run between these two bearings. All bearings must have the same diameter.

b. The fork may have a continuous bearing which runs the whole length of the crankpin. The blade large end bearing runs on the outer face of the fork large end bearing, which must be specially machined to act as a journal.

Articulated Connecting Rod Arrangement

The articulated connecting rod arrangement has a single large end bearing block to which both connecting rods are attached. The master rod is connected rigidly by means of a palm end, while the slave rod is attached by an articulated arrangement, such as a pin and bush. This is necessary because the motions of both pistons, and of their connecting rods and large ends, differ as the crank rotates. The articulated large end arrangement has cylinder centres in line across the engine and both pistons may be removed without touching the large end bearing **(Figure 14)**.

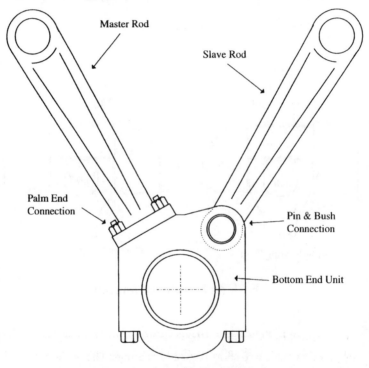

Figure 14. Articulated Connecting Rod

2.3   PISTONS AND PISTON RINGS

Piston Strength

Pistons for medium speed engines must be capable of withstanding the gas loads experienced during peak firing periods without any appreciable leakage. As a result the sealing arrangements provided by the piston rings must be effective even though lubrication at the top of the cylinder may be marginal. Unlike crosshead engines most medium speed engines rely on splash lubrication from the crankcase, which must be controlled by scraper rings located on the piston crown or on the skirt. A skirt **(shown in Figure 15)** is necessary on two stroke cycle engines in order to seal the ports when the piston is at the top of its stroke. In a four stroke engine, the skirt also guides the piston into the cylinder, countering the side thrusts caused by the angularity of the connecting rod.

Piston Assembly

A piston assembly consists essentially of the piston crown, the skirt, a gudgeon pin and a number of piston rings. The crown is subject to the highest combustion pressure and thermal load. It may also suffer from impingement by the combustion flame if the atomiser spray is defective. Piston crowns are of the dished type to provide a combustion chamber between the piston crown and the cylinder head. To give the desired combustion, the shape of the bowl formed in the crown depends on many factors, including the choice of atomiser spray. The flat rim of the piston surrounding the dished combustion chamber generally contains cut-out sections to prevent the piston from hitting the inlet and exhaust valves. The piston crown is generally made from high quality, deformation resistant forged steel and contains internal cooling surfaces and the provision for a number of piston rings. In some engines all piston ring grooves are located in the crown (e.g. MAN-B&W L32/40). In others (e.g. Wärtsilä Vasa 38) only two compression rings are fitted in the crown while a third compression ring and oil scraper ring are located in the upper part of the skirt. The crown may taper slightly in order to allow for thermal expansion while in service. During operation the upper part of the crown becomes hotter than the lower part so it will expand more. Tapering allows a narrow clearance between piston and liner to be maintained **(Figure 15)**.

Piston Skirt

A piston skirt guides the piston in the cylinder, minimising the tipping of the piston which causes high contact pressures at upper and lower parts of the piston/skirt assembly and disturbs gas sealing of the rings. The piston skirt is subject to lower thermal and mechanical loads than the crown and can be made from materials of lower strength. It is subject to greater rubbing against the liner, however, and should have a lower coefficient of friction. Nodular cast-iron is often used for piston skirts due to its low coefficient of friction and ability to be readily cast into a fairly complex shape. Aluminium is also used for piston skirts. Its low density is an advantage in terms of inertia forces, although it has a higher coefficient of thermal expansion than nodular cast iron. At low loads an aluminium skirt will give increased cylinder clearance compared with one of nodular iron, so the piston axis will differ slightly from the cylinder axis. At reduced loads an aluminium skirt will therefore not provide as stable a platform for the piston rings as a nodular iron skirt. The skirt does not need to be perfectly cylindrical, as long as it is shaped to assist the formation of an effective lubricant film between piston and liner. Some skirts taper slightly from bottom to top while others are of oval section, with the minor axis parallel to the axis of the gudgeon pin.

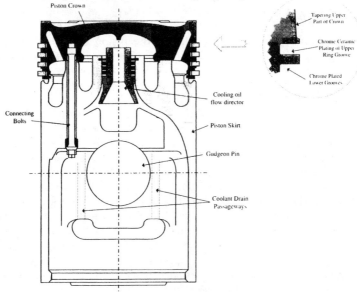

Figure 15. Composite Piston

Piston Gudgeon Pin

The gudgeon pin for the small end bearing is located in the piston skirt. Large diameter pins allow for high cylinder peak pressures without imposing high bearing loads. A pin diameter of about 40 per cent of the cylinder diameter is normal for most current engines. As already discussed in 'Connecting Rods', above, small end bearings are often stepped, which presents a large bearing surface to the lower side of the gudgeon pin. This also allows an increased area of the piston skirt to be in contact with the upper face of the gudgeon pin, reducing piston skirt to gudgeon pin pressures. With such stepped arrangements bending of the gudgeon pin, with its associated edge pressures, is practically eliminated. Gudgeon pins are generally floating in both the connecting rod small end bush and the piston. Where the piston skirt is made from forged aluminium alloy (e.g. MAN-B&W L58/64) no additional bushing is required in the piston, to accommodate the gudgeon pin, as the aluminium acts as a bearing surface. Some cast aluminium pistons have aluminium-bronze bushes. For piston skirts of nodular cast iron some form of brass bushing may be employed, but the self lubricating properties of this material often make it unnecessary. The gudgeon pin is located endwise in the piston skirt by means of circlips or plates bolted to recesses in the skirt. Hollow gudgeon pins are employed, which reduce the weight and provide a useful distribution point for the lubrication, which flows up the connecting rod. Holes in the gudgeon pin distribute the oil to the bearing surfaces **(Figure 16)**.

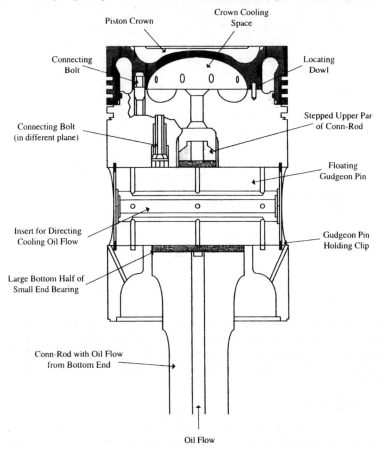

Figure 16. Section through a Piston with a Hollow Gudgeon Pin

Piston Cooling

Piston cooling is necessary to preserve mechanical strength and restrict thermal expansion. Cooling oil circulates around the spaces immediately below the crown. The crown thickness is such that it maintains strength without inducing thermal stress normally associated with large temperature gradients. For small low powered engines a limited amount of oil splashed from the crankcase to the underside of the piston is sufficient to provide the necessary cooling. A more positive effect can be obtained by spraying the oil from a standing spray nozzle in the crankcase to the underside of the piston crown. For highly rated engines a more positive coolant flow is required and this comes from the pressure circulation system via the main bearings, crankshaft and connecting rod. Because of the inertia forces in the connecting rod as the crankshaft rotates, the supply of oil to the piston cooling cavity is not constant, which does not matter provided a total supply rate in the order of 7.5 litres/kWh can be maintained. A 'cocktail shaker' effect form of cooling is employed which enables the coolant to reach all parts of the piston crown cavity, providing a very effective means of removing heat. The cooling cavity is not completely full of oil, it also contains air. As the piston reciprocates the oil is washed to all parts, even those blind areas where normal circulation could not extend. Because of the 'cocktail shaker' effect it does not matter that the coolant flow rate is not constant. Coolant from the crown cavity falls back to the crankcase through a number of holes in the piston skirt.

Aluminium Piston

An all-aluminium piston is used in some engines, particularly those operating at higher speeds. A cast aluminium alloy is employed. Because of the thick section, the piston has sufficient strength to resist pressure loads, except at the upper ring grooves. To prevent damage to these grooves from the high gas loadings on the rings, a nickel alloy cast-iron insert is fitted covering the first one or two ring grooves. Cooling oil circulates through a cast-in stainless steel cooling coil. The casting-in of the coil is made possible by the lower melting temperature of aluminium. Aluminium has a relatively high coefficient of thermal expansion and due to the temperature differential between the top of the piston and the bottom it is necessary to design aluminium pistons which taper from bottom to top to obtain a parallel form at working temperatures **(Figure 17)**.

Rotating Piston

Sulzer 'Z' engines are fitted with pistons that rotate as they reciprocate. A number of advantages are claimed for this arrangement including the avoidance of local overheating due to piston ring blow-past and improved cylinder lubrication. It also acts as a safeguard against scuffing as a new oil wetted portion of the piston is in contact with the pressure side of the liner at each stroke. A rotating piston requires a spherical small end, rather like a ball and socket joint. This provides equal support of the piston crown at all radial sections, unlike the gudgeon pin arrangement which has better support along the axis of the gudgeon pin. Piston to liner clearance is governed by the maximum amount of piston distortion during peak pressure periods. As this is less with a spherical small end, use of the Sulzer rotating piston means that reduced piston to liner clearance may be employed. Smaller running clearances also allow the oil scraper ring to be positioned low down on the piston skirt. It is claimed that this stabilises lubricating oil consumption over long periods **(see Figure 18)**.

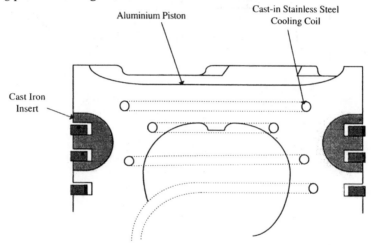

Figure 17. Aluminium Piston with Cast-In Cooling Coil

Rotating Mechanism

Rotation of the piston is produced by the swing of the connecting rod as the piston reciprocates. Within the spherical small end at the axis of rotation is a hole containing a bush. Held in the bush are two spring loaded pawls, one on each side, which engage by means of a spring arrangement with a toothed ratchet ring held in the body of the piston. As the connecting rod swings it causes the bush, and hence the pawls, to oscillate. The double pawls act alternately on opposite sides of the toothed ratchet ring to produce rotation of the piston. The spring reduces forces in the ratchet mechanism and allows a smooth motion. Piston rotation rates depends on the size of the engine and its operating speed; e.g. at an engine speed of 510 rev/min the piston of a ZA40S engine rotates at about 9 rev/min **(see Figure 19)**.

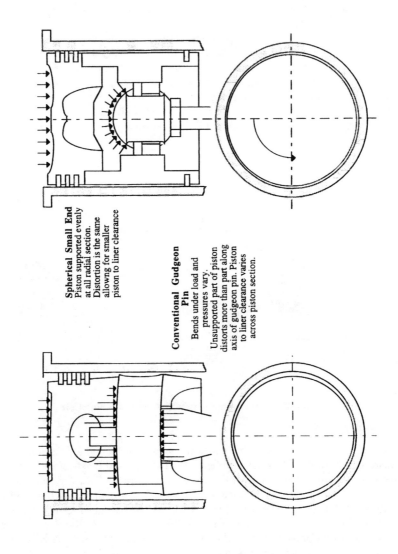

Spherical Small End
Piston supported evenly at all radial section. Distortion is the same allowng for smaller piston to liner clearance

Conventional Gudgeon Pin
Bends under load and pressures vary. Unsupported part of piston distorts more than part along axis of gudgeon pin. Piston to liner clearance varies across piston section.

Figure 18. Conventional Gudgeon Pin and Spherical Small End

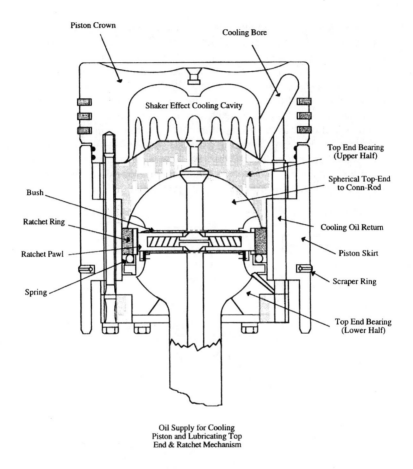

Piston Crown

Cooling Bore

Shaker Effect Cooling Cavity

Top End Bearing
(Upper Half)

Spherical Top-End
to Conn-Rod

Bush

Ratchet Ring

Cooling Oil Return

Ratchet Pawl

Piston Skirt

Spring

Scraper Ring

Top End Bearing
(Lower Half)

Oil Supply for Cooling
Piston and Lubricating Top
End & Ratchet Mechanism

Figure 19. Section through Rotating Piston

Spherical Small End Bearing

The two part spherical small end must be accurately machined. It is kept lubricated by means of oil flowing up a hole in the connecting rod from the large end. The main portion of the oil flow passes to the piston cooling cavity where a 'cocktail shaker' effect form of cooling is employed. Oil is also taken from the main flow in order to lubricate the ratchet mechanism.

Piston Rings

Piston rings are critical to engine performance as they are required to seal the piston and maintain gas pressure. The upper ring in particular is subject to extreme operating conditions in terms of temperature and pressure. Rings must have a spring to ensure they act outwards, initially bringing them into contact with the liner. As gas pressure in the cylinder increases during compression and combustion, the gas pressure acts on the ring's upper face and back face, ensuring the ring is held firmly at the bottom of the groove, and that there is sufficient force to keep it in contact with the oil film on the liner; this prevents gas blowpast and ring collapse. Ring collapse takes place if gas pressure acts on the front face of the ring. This will occur if there are uneven wear patterns on the liner surface or if the ring loses its initial spring and does not retain contact with the liner surface **(Figure 20)**.

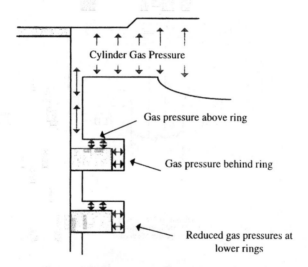

Cylinder Gas Pressure

Gas pressure above ring

Gas pressure behind ring

Reduced gas pressures at lower rings

Figure 20. Gas Pressures acting on Piston Rings

Piston Ring Clearance

Rings require a clearance in their grooves to ensure they are free to move. This clearance should be as small as possible to ensure that the rings remain squarely in the grooves. Too large an axial clearance may cause the rings to twist as gas pressure increases. This can cause a sharp edge at the corner of the ring to remove the oil film from the liner, resulting in excessive wear or even ring breakage. Too little clearance may result in the build-up of deposits in the ring grooves causing the rings to jam. Sufficient radial clearance is needed to ensure that the ring can move inwards during passage over unworn parts of the liner while still retaining a reservoir allowing the gas to act on the back of the ring. A split in the circumference of each ring is required in order to enable it to be fitted in the groove in the piston. The correct ring expanders should always be used when fitting rings in order to ensure stresses are kept within limits on all parts of the rings, and to ensure safety. Butt clearances are generally angled and rings are inserted with the angles facing in opposite directions for alternate rings. Gas flows past the rings at the butts. Having as small a butt clearance as possible limits any pressure drop, while having the angles in opposite directions makes the leakage path more complex. As rings rotate in their grooves during engine operation it is unlikely that all butts will ever be lined up together, however angled butts mean that there would be no simple leakage path even if they did all come close together. Too large a butt clearance causes increased gas leakage, while insufficient butt clearance can cause the butts to come together as the ring expands in service, leading to jamming of the ring and possible seizure **(Figure 21)**.

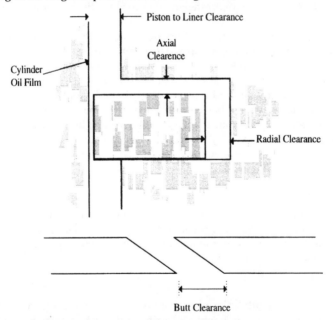

Figure 21. Piston Ring Clearances

Piston Ring Materials

In most engines the top three rings are classed as compression rings, although the upper ring takes most of the gas loading. Ring materials should be compatible with the liner material in order to avoid scuffing as the rings rub over the liner surface. Rings must retain their initial spring at operational temperatures and pressures, resist thermal cracking and maintain their mechanical strength. Ideally they should have some self lubricating properties. Cast iron is an ideal material but for modern conditions alloying elements such as manganese, chromium and molybdenum are employed to improve mechanical strength, heat resistance and self-lubrication. Plain rings are rare, and coatings and/or profiling are employed to provide necessary properties as required. Chromium plating of the rubbing faces of compression rings is common to many engine builders as this reduces ring wear and improves operating characteristics. In some cases (e.g. MAN-B&W L58/64 engines) chrome-ceramic plating is used for the first compression ring due to the severe operating conditions experienced. Chromium faced rings should never be used with chromium plated cylinder liners as the action of chrome rubbing against chrome results in the layers being torn away. In some cases bronze inlays are used or the chromium plating is recessed below the outer cast iron edges; both arrangements speed up the running-in process as the bronze or cast iron will quickly wear and the ring will take up the ideal shape for the cylinder. Some rings are profiled or tapered on the outer face in order to reduce the running-in time. The engine can be subjected to full load when there is a reasonable width of ring face in contact with the liner surface. A full width contact is not necessary, nor is it usually possible, as rings twist slightly in their grooves and have a barrel shaped profile which allows the build-up of an oil wedge between the ring and liner on the up and down strokes of the piston. Profiles and tapers may not be readily noticed and inserting the ring incorrectly can have a detrimental effect on the cylinder performance. Some manufacturers mark such rings so that they can be inserted correctly **(Figure 22)**.

Chromium Plating of Rings

Chromium plating is used to prevent the buildup of carbon deposits in ring grooves or on the surfaces of rings in those grooves, as such deposits do not adhere readily to chrome. Either the ring grooves or the upper and lower faces of the rings may be plated.

Oil Scraper Rings

Oil scraper rings regulate the oil layer on the surface of the liner and minimise lubricating oil consumption while ensuring sufficient coverage to restrict ring and liner wear and maintain a seal between rings and liner. Scraper rings are fitted low on the piston or piston skirt so they are not subject to high gas temperatures or pressures. Although plain rings, suitably profiled, have proved effective in the past, most modern highly rated engines employ spring loaded scraper rings. The advantage of such rings is that the spring is able to maintain an even pressure against the liner surface, while the ring may be of a thin radial section allowing it to deform readily and so maintain contact with a worn or distorted liner which may no longer be of circular section. Passageways are generally provided in the piston skirt so the oil scraped off the liner drains back to the crankcase inside the piston skirt and not down the liner.

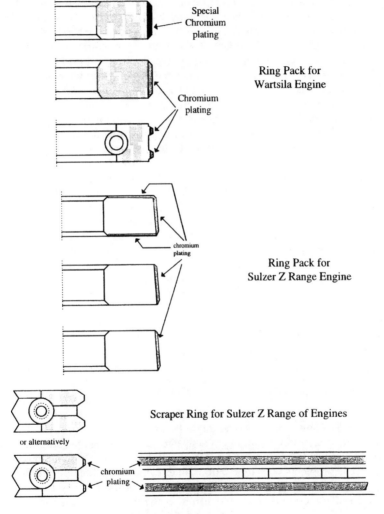

Special Chromium plating

Ring Pack for Wartsila Engine

Chromium plating

chromium plating

Ring Pack for Sulzer Z Range Engine

Scraper Ring for Sulzer Z Range of Engines

or alternatively

chromium plating

Figure 22. Piston Ring Profiles

2.4   Cylinder Liners

Cylinder Liner Design

Cylinder liners are centrifugally cast from nodular or close grained cast iron to obtain good mechanical strength and wear resistance. A rigid liner bore which is free of distortion is ideal and, with the provision of good lubrication, provides optimum running conditions for the piston and piston rings. Liners fit into the cylinder block, but for many highly rated engines the cylinder block does not always house the water jacket, which is instead provided by means of a separate unit mounted above the block. Such an arrangement provides cooling just where it is required, at the upper part of the cylinder liner, and also avoids the risk of cooling water leaking into the crankcase or of oil from the crankcase gaining entry to the cooling water system. The liner is located within this jacket unit and sealing rings are provided to prevent water leakage. The jacket unit sits on the cylinder block and is held in place by the cylinder head. Although such jackets may not be shrink fits with the liner they should be neat fits and add strength to the upper part of the liner under working conditions. Individual jackets ensure low cylinder liner distortion and prevent any one cylinder causing distortion of neighbouring cylinders. The liners must be a neat fit in the cylinder block to prevent distortion. For two stroke engines it is essential that the correct angular position is obtained, so exhaust and air inlet ports are aligned with their respective passages. Sealing rings are still provided between the liner and the cylinder block, even though there may be no water jacket in the block, to prevent oil leaking into the cylinder block section. Where the cylinder block provides a water jacket for the cylinder liner, sealing rings are required at the lower part of the liner. Some sealing arrangement is also needed in the liner above the jacket. It is usual to provide a tell-tale between the two lower sealing rings, so that water leaking past the upper seal ring or oil leaking past the lower ring may be readily detected. An alternative to having a jacket around the upper part of the liner is to have a solid upper section liner of the desired thickness for strength, and to provide some sort of cooling, usually bore cooling **(Figure 23)**.

Cylinder Liner Stress

The upper part of the liner is subject to high mechanical stresses due to peak cylinder pressures and also to high thermal loading. The cylinder wall temperature should be kept high enough to safeguard against sulphuric acid corrosion when burning fuels containing sulphur, but too high a temperature will cause problems with lubrication. Inner cylinder wall temperatures in the region of 185°C – measured at top dead centre of the first piston ring – are used for many engines available during at the time of writing (e.g. Wärtsilä Vasa 32). Cooling is essential but does cause thermal stress which, when added to the high mechanically induced stress resulting from high cylinder pressures, may lead to problems. The mechanically induced stress varies during operation, and fatigue cracking may result if such stresses are too high. Cooling produces a temperature gradient across the wall of the liner between the hot inner surface and the colder cooled surface; the larger the temperature gradient the higher the thermally induced stress. The colder side is subject to a tensile stress as it is stretched by expansion of the hot side, while the hot side is subject to compressive stress due to restricted thermal expansion. A thin wall section has lower thermal stress since most of the temperature change takes place in the fluid and not in the wall section. However, for a thick wall section, relatively little temperature change takes place in the fluid and most is across the wall section. Thus there are larger temperature gradients in the material for thicker wall sections than for thin wall sections. During operation it is important for cooling water temperatures to be maintained within very narrow limits, and not allowed to change rapidly, as this results in large temperature gradients and thermal stresses **(see Figure 24)**.

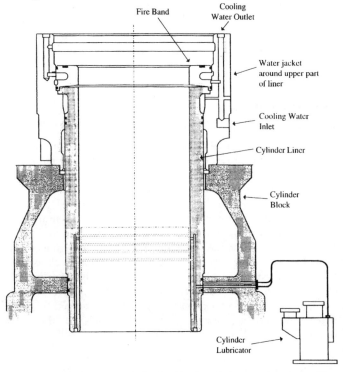

Figure 23. Cylinder Liner, Cylinder Block and Water Jacket Assembly

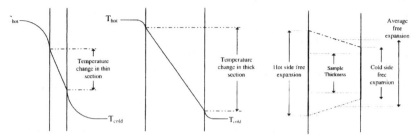

**Figure 24. Temperature Variation across a Cooled Section
and Resultant Thermal Stress**

Bore Cooling

Highly rated engines need thick wall liner upper sections in order to combat pressure stress. This can be seen from the hoop stress equation:

$$\sigma = \frac{Pd}{2t}$$

Where:

σ = Stress (N/m^2)

P = Pressure (N/m^2)

d = Cylinder bore (m)

t = wall thickness (m)

For a constant bore engine to keep the same stress for increased peak pressure, wall thickness must be increased. Similarly, to increase the bore for the same peak pressure and stress, the wall thickness must also be increased. In both cases higher thermal stress would result if the coolant was circulated around the outer surface of the liner. This may be solved by bore cooling. With this system a number of small bore holes, about 10mm diameter, are drilled in the liner wall close to the inner surface. Water is circulated through these holes, thereby extracting heat from close to the hot inner surface of the liner wall. The remaining section of the liner can be as thick as necessary to withstand the mechanical stress as its temperature will be fairly constant. The coolant path though the bores may be straight from an inlet connection to an outlet, or may be more complex employing blind or plugged connecting holes to give a complete cooling system which interconnects with the cylinder head **(Figure 25)**.

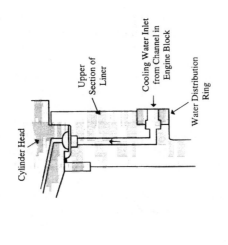

Cylinder Head

Upper Section of Liner

Cooling Water Inlet from Channel in Engine Block

Water Distribution Ring

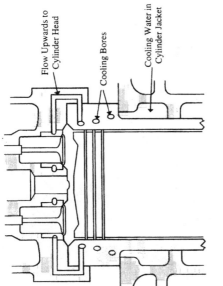

Flow Upwards to Cylinder Head

Cooling Bores

Cooling Water in Cylinder Jacket

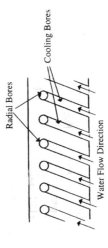

Radial Bores

Cooling Bores

Water Flow Direction

Section through upper part of liner

Figure 25. Bore Cooling Arrangements

Anti-Polishing Rings

Anti-polishing rings are fitted by many engine builders to prevent bore polishing during operation. Cylinder combustion, particularly when burning residual fuels, produces carbon which has a tendency to build up around the upper edges of the piston and down the side towards the first piston ring. This carbon will eventually build up to the extent that it touches the liner surface, removing the lubricating oil film and polishing the surface. Carbon may even extend to the first ring groove where it will cause jamming of the ring. An insert in the upper part of the liner, known as an anti-polishing ring (Wärtsilä and Sulzer) or a fire band (MAN-B&W) has a slightly smaller bore than the cylinder liner but a slightly larger bore than the upper part of the piston and the anti-polishing ring extends almost to the upper face of the first piston ring when the piston is a top dead centre. Any carbon which builds up on the piston edge is removed by the anti-polishing ring as the piston reciprocates so it never extends to the liner surface. Polishing of the liner gives a highly glazed surface to which the lubricating oil cannot adhere, so an effective lubricant film cannot form on the liner. The anti-polishing ring ensures a good lubricant film on the liner surface thereby reducing ring and liner wear and giving a more consistent lubricating oil consumption **(Figures 26 and 27)**.

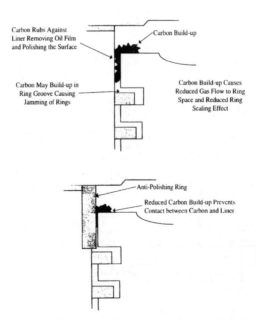

Figure 26. Liner Polishing Mechanism and the Anti-Polishing Ring

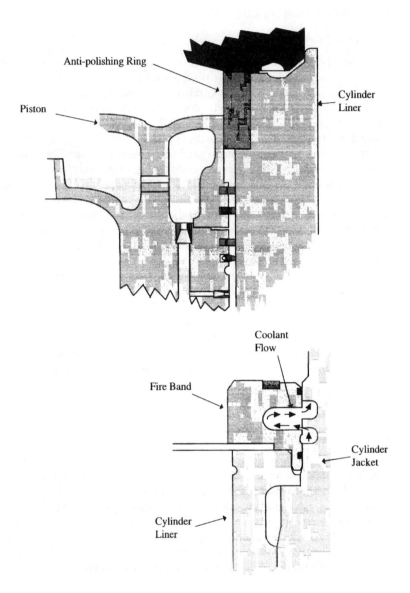

Figure 27. Anti-Polishing Systems for Cylinder Liners

2.5   CYLINDER HEAD

CYLINDER HEAD CONSTRUCTION

The cylinder head must effectively close the upper part of the cylinder and provide space for air inlet and exhaust valves, a fuel injector and a number of other fittings such as air start valve, relief valve and indicator cock. In Vee type engines it is usual to fit air start valves to one bank of cylinders only. The head must resist mechanical stress due to peak firing pressure and must also be cooled to maintain strength. As with cylinder liners, cooling can present problems related to thermal stress and an effective system of coolant circulation is needed. Although many cylinder heads still employ cored-out cooling spaces, some engines (e.g. Sulzer 'Z' range) make use of bore cooling systems. In some cases combined bore and cavity cooling is used, with the bores located at the lower face closest to the combustion chamber where the cooling effect is critical. This lower face is known as the 'flame plate'. The cylinder head sits on the top of the liner and holds it in place. A number of hydraulically tightened studs are usually employed to hold the head onto the cylinder block. Cooling water flows from the cylinder liner to the cylinder head either directly, with self sealing connections, or by means of connecting pipes. Water outlet flow is from the top of the head to a common flow pipe. Some form of air vent arrangement is usually provided at the water outlet pipe to ensure removal of air from the coolant passageways following overhaul. For most engines each unit, cylinder liner jacket and head, can be isolated from the coolant circulating system so it is only necessary to drain the unit being overhauled. The cylinder head also connects to the air inlet and exhaust trunkings; passageways are cast into the cylinder head to permit the flow of combustion air and exhaust gas.

Cylinder Head Materials

Spheroidal graphite, or nodular, cast-iron is often used for cylinder heads, as its relatively high mechanical strength and ease of casting are ideal for the purpose. The cylinder head is a relatively complex casting due to the presence of a number of valve pockets, air inlet and exhaust gas passageways, and cooling water spaces. Rigidity in design is essential to ensure the head retains a uniform seal with the liner, while a rigid flame plate also means there will be no deformation of the valve seat areas. A metallic joint is placed at the mating faces between the head and the liner to ensure effective sealing.

Cylinder Head Design

The actual design of the cylinder head depends on a number of factors including – but not limited to – the operating cycle. A two stroke cycle engine will generally have air inlet ports in the liner, so no air inlet valves are fitted in the head, If exhaust ports are used there will only be an injector, air start valve, relief valve and indicator cock in the cylinder head. Many four stroke engines now employ multiple air inlet and exhaust valves in order to improve performance. During the exhaust stroke the piston forces the exhaust gas from the cylinder and the gas exerts a back pressure on the piston. Pumping work is expended in removing the gas so the higher the back pressure, the greater the pumping work done. A large exhaust valve area with large exhaust passages minimises this loss of useful work. During the suction stroke, air flows into the cylinder as the piston moves downwards but if the air inlet valve area is small the air pressure in the cylinder at the end of the suction stroke will be lower than it would have been had there been unrestricted air flow. For these reasons, cross-sectional areas of air inlet and exhaust valves should be as large as possible. However, single air inlet and exhaust valves must have maximum diameters slightly less than half the diameter of the cylinder. Multiple valves are employed to give larger valve areas. The use of two exhaust or air inlet valves provides a larger flow area, although the actual individual valves will be smaller than a single valve. Two valves also give a better flow pattern in the cylinder, while allowing improved distribution of internal strengthening ribs and a centrally positioned injector **(Figure 28)**.

Valves and Lift

Both exhaust and air inlet valves must be actuated together and the valve clearance of both must be correctly adjusted. Valves, particularly the exhaust valves, expand in service and clearance must be provided between the rocker and valve stem to allow for this. If there is too little clearance, the valve will not close fully when it is at operating condition, leading to loss of power and damage to the valve and seat from escaping high pressure/temperature gas. Too much clearance will slightly reduce lift but will cause hammering between the rocker and valve stem faces, resulting in damage. Double valves may be actuated from a single push rod in several ways, including a forked rocker, twin rockers and a yoke actuating two valves. The lift of any valve gives maximum flow when it equals $D/4$, where D is the valve diameter. Valve lift is therefore set by the valve diameter and any greater lift than $D/4$ is unnecessary **(Figures 29 and 30)**.

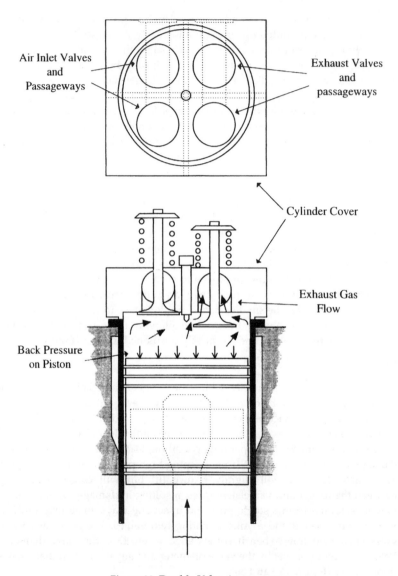

Air Inlet Valves
and
Passageways

Exhaust Valves
and
passageways

Cylinder Cover

Exhaust Gas
Flow

Back Pressure
on Piston

Figure 28. Double Valve Arrangement

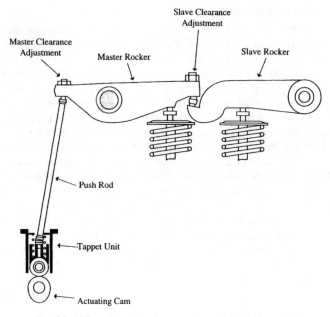

Figure 29. Double Valve Actuating System - Master and Slave Rocker Type

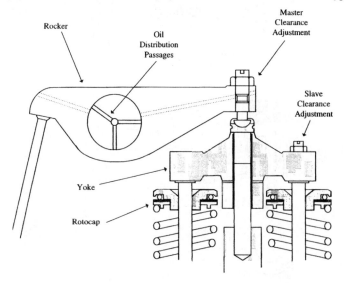

Figure 30. Yoke Type Double Valve Actuating System

Hydraulic Valve Actuation

Hydraulic actuation of valves is common in crosshead engines but not in medium speed engines. However, the Sulzer ZA50S engine employs such a system. There are no rockers, and so no valve clearances to set, and thermal expansion is accounted for by the leak-off of oil from the hydraulic system. The hydraulic pump unit is driven by the camshaft. Pressure oil acts on the balancing piston which in turn directs the pressure oil to the hydraulic cylinders, to open both valves together. The balancing piston ensures that both valves have the same lift and timing. The closing of the air inlet valves can be changed to vary the cylinder air charge, which gives control over fuel economy, smoke generation and exhaust emissions over the entire power range. During normal operation the control valve shuts off the delivery line when the actuator pump reaches the end of its stroke, so the air inlet valves remain open until the hydraulic pump piston uncovers the suction port and the delivery line remains pressurised until then. Pneumatic movement of the control valve to the open position allows oil in the delivery line to be drawn back into the actuator cylinder, causing the inlet valves to close earlier than they would have done had the control valve remained closed **(Figures 31 and 32)**.

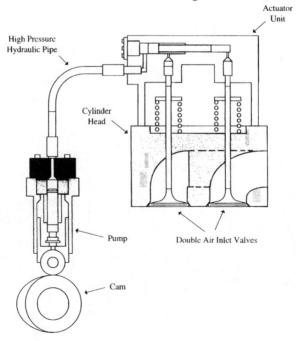

Figure 31. Sulzer Hydraulic Variable Inlet Valve Closing (VIC) System

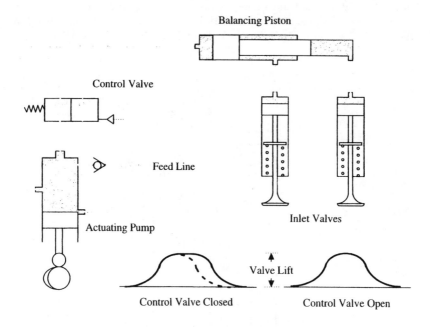

Balancing Piston

Control Valve

Feed Line

Actuating Pump

Inlet Valves

Valve Lift

Control Valve Closed   Control Valve Open

Figure 32. Sulzer VIC System

Caged Valves

Air inlet and exhaust valves operate in the same way and their design is fundamentally the same. Because of the aggressive environment in which the exhaust valves operate, however, they require better materials for their seats and usually have additional mechanisms which allow for rotation in service. Valves open into the cylinder, with coil springs providing a closing force. By opening into the cylinder, as pressure builds up during compression and firing, the pressure acting on the valve head increases the sealing force. The spring force must be sufficient to allow the valve to form an effective initial seal against its seat. Some valves are fitted directly in the cylinder head while others are mounted in cages which fit into pockets in the head. The advantage of caged valves is that they may be removed for overhaul without removing the cylinder head, reducing maintenance time. Exhaust valves generally have the shortest operating interval between overhaul of all engine components apart from fuel injectors. The problem with caged valves is that the cage takes up space in the cylinder head, which reduces the effective valve area and means that additional connections are needed in the cylinder head. However, in certain engines (e.g. MAN-B&W V48/60) the exhaust valves are caged but the air inlet valves are fitted directly in the cylinder head **(Figure 33)**.

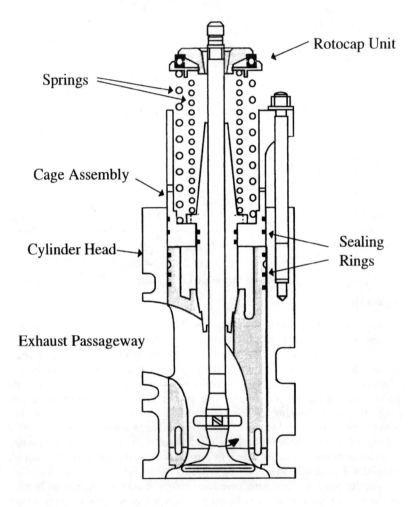

Rotocap Unit

Springs

Cage Assembly

Cylinder Head

Sealing Rings

Exhaust Passageway

Figure 33. Caged Valve

Exhaust Valve Seats

Valve seats for exhaust valves must be able to withstand the highly corrosive environment in which they work, particularly with respect to the vanadium slag deposits which form on the seats when burning residual fuels. These deposits are highly corrosive and adhere tenaciously to any material which operates at or above the solidification temperature of the slag, making the seat area particularly susceptible. The slag forms due to the combustion of vanadium and the solidification temperature of the slag is reduced in the presence of sodium, a critical ratio of 3:1 vanadium to sodium giving the lowest solidification temperature. It is extremely difficult to avoid vanadium in modern residual fuels and the engine designer must take steps to minimise the problem, including cooling of the seat area and the use of resistant materials. Whether exhaust valves are in cages or fitted directly into the cylinder cover, the seat area is cooled by water circulating in passageways close to the seat. The reduction in seat temperature means the molten slag is less likely to stick. The seat section is often separate from the cage, or cylinder head, depending on valve type, as this allows it to be made from corrosion and heat resistant material such as molybdenum steel. To make the entire cage or head from that material would be unnecessarily costly. Some valve seats have special stellite inserts to resist the corrosive and abrasive action of the exhaust gas. Valves are constructed from a corrosion and heat resistant material such as nimonic.

Valve Rotation

The life of the exhaust valve may be also prolonged by valve rotation. By rotating the exhaust valve in service the risk of local overheating, and consequent distortion and vanadium buildup can be avoided. This also prevents any deposits on the seat being hammered into the same spot on the valve.

Rotocap Unit

Rotocap units fitted to the valve stem, generally the upper part, produce rotation of the valve by about 8° during the opening period. The valve cover contains a number of ramped slots, usually seven, each housing a spring loaded ball bearing. These ball bearings run on a disc supported on a 'Belleville' washer. This washer makes contact with the spring carrier at its outer edge and with the valve cover at its inner edge, preventing rotation of the valve. As force is applied to the valve for opening, the Belleville washer is collapsed, removing the frictional contact between the spring carrier and the valve cover. This cover is then supported on the ball bearings and is free to rotate. Further increase in force on the valve as it opens acts through the ball bearings, which tend to move down the ramped slots – or rather the ramped slots move over the ball bearings – producing the rotation. As soon as the valve begins to close the force on the valve is reduced and the Belleville washer restores frictional contact between the spring carrier and the cover, preventing further rotation. When the valve has closed the load on the ball bearing is removed and the springs return them to their original positions ready for the next opening cycle **(Figure 34)**.

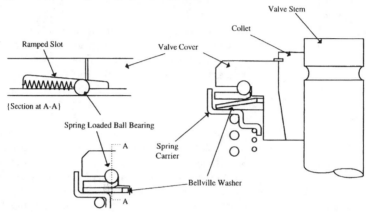

Figure 34. Rotocap Valve Rotator

Valve Stem Spinners

Spinners on the valve stem bring about rotation due to the action of the exhaust gas. Spinners are effectively gas turbine blades fitted on the stem and they rotate the valve during the entire period when exhaust gas is flowing. This rotation not only repositions the valve relative to its seat but also means that the valve is rotating as it reseats. This rotation provides a light grinding effect which removes deposits that have built up on the seating faces during that opening period. The frictional contact between the cylinder head and the valve stem via the springs must be removed to allow rotation. This is achieved by interposing a ball bearing system between the valve cover and spring such that as soon as the valve leaves its seat it is floating on the bearing and is free to rotate **(Figure 35)**.

Cylinder Relief Valves

Cylinder relief valves are fitted to release excess pressure and ensure the gudgeon pin and large end bearings are not overloaded. Such overload could cause serious damage. High peak pressures generally result from the early injection of fuel or a defective fuel injector. Cylinder relief valves are basically spring loaded valves held within their own cages, which are bolted to the cylinder head. The relief valve vents to atmosphere and the valve itself need only be small as the release of a relatively small amount of gas can reduce the cylinder pressure to an acceptable level. The noise created by the lift of a relief valve gives notice to the engineer that something is wrong, so the valve is a warning device as well as a safety device. The same passage which connects the relief valve to the combustion chamber is often used to connect the indicator cock with the cylinder, thereby saving on the number of openings into the cylinder and the number of passageways in the head.

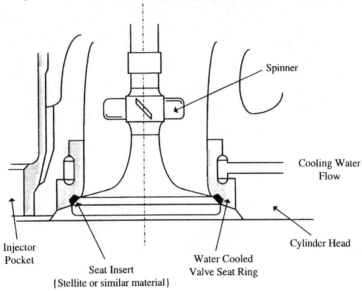

Spinner

Cooling Water Flow

Cylinder Head

Injector Pocket

Seat Insert {Stellite or similar material}

Water Cooled Valve Seat Ring

Figure 35. Valve Rotating Spinner System

Air Start Valves

Air start valves are required for most medium speed engines to enable them to start. Some small engines have pneumatic turning motors which connect with gear teeth on the flywheel but the more usual means of starting an engine is by means of compressed air directed to the cylinders through valves. The non return starting air valve is actuated by pilot air from a distributor which gives the correct sequence and timing of the starting air valves. Flame traps are fitted in the main air line immediately before the starting air valve to restrict the risk of flame propagating back to the air start line in the event of blowback.

2.6 CAMSHAFT, CAMS AND VALVE OPERATING MECHANISMS

Camshafts

Camshafts carry cams which operate the fuel pumps as well as the inlet and exhaust valves; the camshaft also drives the starting air distributor, governor and overspeed trip. Camshafts are provided for both banks of Vee type engines, and in some cases separate camshafts are provided for operating the valves and the fuel pumps. Four stroke cycle engines have camshaft which rotate at half engine speed, because there is one operating cycle for every two engine revolutions. Camshafts of two stroke cycle engines rotate at engine speed. In some engines vibration dampers are fitted at the free ends of camshafts, but not all engines require such equipment. Camshaft drive is generally achieved by means of gear wheels from the crankshaft, but some engines do employ chain drive systems. If a propulsion engine is required to reverse, a reversing system will be fitted which enables valves, pumps, etc. to be retimed for rotation in the opposite direction. This would involve axial movement of the camshaft or rotation of the cams relative to the crankshaft. However, the majority of medium speed propulsion engines employ electric drives or gearing with Controllable Pitch (CP) propellers thus they are nor required to reverse. Along its length, the forged camshaft will be supported on a number of bearings, usually one bearing between each cylinder unit. Wärtsilä engines are provided with camshafts made from single cylinder elements bolted together. Each drop forged camshaft element comprises integral cams and separate bearing journals. Individual elements are joined by flange connections to form a complete camshaft. This form of construction allows for lateral dismantling and enables damaged sections to be replaced as necessary **(Figure 36)**.

Cams

Separate forged cams are used by some engine builders – Sulzer, for example. These cams are shrunk on to the camshaft hydraulically and can be removed or repositioned hydraulically. Such a system enables cams, particularly those for fuel pumps, to be retimed. MAN-B&W L+V32/40 engines have fuel pump actuating camshafts which can be adjusted to optimise injection timing. Axial movement of the stub axle which contains the final gear wheel causes a slight relative rotation of the camshaft, as the drive from the gearwheel to the camshaft is by means of angled splines. Retiming of the complete fuel pump camshaft can be accomplished while the engine is in operation **(Figure 37)**.

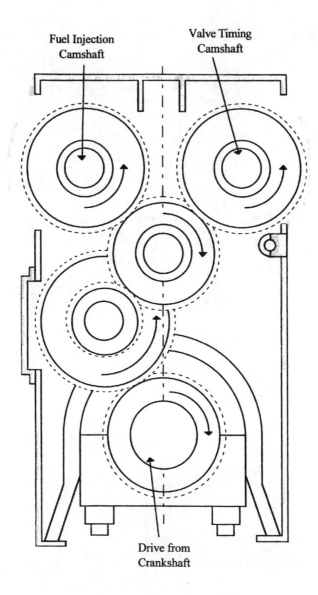

Figure 36. Camshaft Gearwheel Drive Arrangement

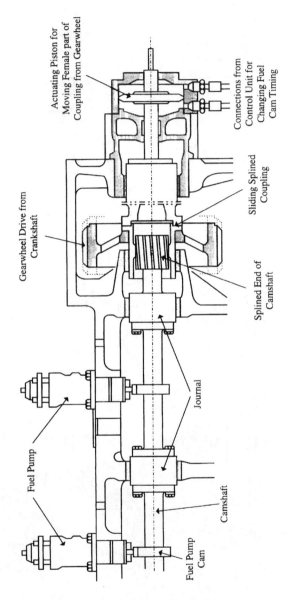

Figure 37. MAN-B&W Fuel Pump Camshaft Arrangement

Cam Shape

Cams are shaped so as to give the required rate of lift for the fuel pump plunger and for opening the valves; the rate of closing is also governed by the shape of the cam. Running faces of cams are hardened to increase resistance to wear. Cam followers consist of a roller in a spring- or hydraulically- damped tappet unit, which slides in a guide within the camshaft housing. Damping permits smoother operation and limits the risk of impact damage between cam and roller; loads on fuel pump cams and followers can be very high. An abundant oil supply should always be available to the cam box in order to provide an adequate oil film between the cam and follower and at the tappet. Contact between the cam and its follower should always be of the rolling type and frequent checks are required at these surfaces to detect signs of scuffing.

Engine Fuel Injection Systems

Fuel injection systems for medium speed engines are complex. The fuel injection pump, high pressure pipe and injectors need to be closely matched to provide optimum fuel injection. All parts are critical to performance and a slight deterioration in any can have adverse effects on cylinder combustion and the operating life of other components in the system. Although items such as pumps and injectors will be considered separately it must be remembered that the fuel injection system is a matched system, not simply a collection of parts.

Jerk Pump Fuel Injection Systems

Medium speed engines operate on the jerk pump fuel injection system in which each cylinder has its own fuel pump supplying high pressure fuel to a fuel injector fitted in the cylinder head. In some cases there may be more than one injector but the majority of engines have one injector per cylinder. The fuel pump is actuated by means of a cam fitted to the camshaft, which also governs injection timing. Fuel pumps are of the helical control type. The high pressure (HP) pipe carrying fuel to the injector is sheathed to prevent fuel leakage in the event of HP pipe failure, particularly as maximum pressures in the HP pipe can reach 2000 bar. Sheathed fuel pipes are a requirement if the engine operates in Unmanned Machinery Space (UMS) mode. Engines may operate on distillate fuel, diesel oil or gas oil, but many highly rated engines employed for propulsion burn residual fuel. In some cases blended fuel is used to reduce the viscosity. It should be noted that blending is carried out in order to reduce the viscosity of the fuel, but levels of damaging impurities such as sulphur and vanadium will not be reduced by the same percentage as the viscosity. The burning of residual or blended fuel requires a heater in the fuel supply line together with lagging on pipes. This ensures the fuel remains at the required viscosity achieve the correct atomisation at the injectors. Some form of fuel treatment, e.g. centrifugal separation, is needed prior to the supply of fuel to the engine.

Helical Control Fuel Pump

Although there are differences between individual designs, all jerk type fuel pumps employing helical control operate on the same fundamental principle. A plunger reciprocates in the barrel of the pump, and clearances are very fine to prevent leakage. Delivery of the fuel takes place when the pressure lifts the discharge valve fitted in the pump cover. Upwards movement of the plunger is achieved by the cam acting through the follower and fuel pump tappet. The tappet is spring loaded to provide a downward movement of the plunger, giving a suction stroke. The actual stroke of the fuel pump plunger is the total lift of the plunger, and is equal to the distance between the cam base circle and the cam peak. However, fuel may not be delivered for the entire duration of the plunger stroke. The portion of the stroke during which fuel is delivered is called the effective stroke and it comes to an end when spill takes place. Spill occurs when the high pressure part of the pump cylinder with the spill port. It results in a rapid drop in fuel delivery pressure and consequent closing of the fuel injector needle valve. The rotational position of the plunger regulates the point in the stroke at which spill takes place, and the plunger is rotated by means of a rack and pinion mechanism actuated by the fuel control.

Helical Control Plunger

Helical control plungers allow the quantity of fuel being delivered and the power generated in the cylinder to be varied. Movement of the control rack rotates the pinion which forms part of a sleeve. This sleeve engages with a rectangular section near the foot of the fuel pump plunger. At the top of the plunger is a helical groove cut in the side, with a vertical groove at the mating ends of the helical groove. In most cases there are actually two sets of grooves diametrically opposite each other providing balance when spill occurs. When the spill port is uncovered there is a sudden drop in oil pressure acting on the side of the plunger, in the annular space below the helix, which forces the plunger against the pump barrel. By providing two identical sets of grooves diametrically opposite each other the pressure forces are balanced, which minimises wear. When the vertical groove is in line with the spill port no oil pressure is produced when the plunger moves upwards and oil can simply flow to spill. This is the no load position of the pump. Rotating the plunger so that the groove is covered by the side of the plunger above the helix means that fuel can be delivered. Delivery commences as soon as the top of the plunger covers the spill port. Pressurised oil will flow down the vertical groove and occupy the annular space below the helix, but will remain pressurised as it cannot escape. Delivery of fuel continues until the helix uncovers the spill port allowing the pressure oil in the annular space and in the space above the plunger top to flow to spill. When this happens delivery of oil to the injector immediately ceases, although the plunger will still be moving upwards. The length of the effective stroke, and hence the amount of fuel delivered, is changed by rotating the plunger and allowing the helix to uncover the spill port earlier in the plunger stroke for less fuel or later in the stroke for more fuel **(Figures 38, 39 and 40)**.

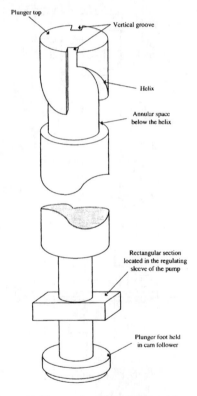

Figure 38. Plunger for Helical Control Pump

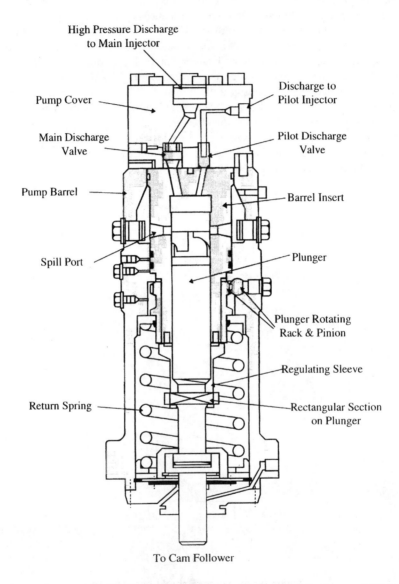

High Pressure Discharge
to Main Injector

Discharge to
Pilot Injector

Pump Cover

Main Discharge
Valve

Pilot Discharge
Valve

Pump Barrel

Barrel Insert

Spill Port

Plunger

Plunger Rotating
Rack & Pinion

Regulating Sleeve

Return Spring

Rectangular Section
on Plunger

To Cam Follower

Figure 39. Assembled Helical Control Fuel Pump (with pilot injection capability)

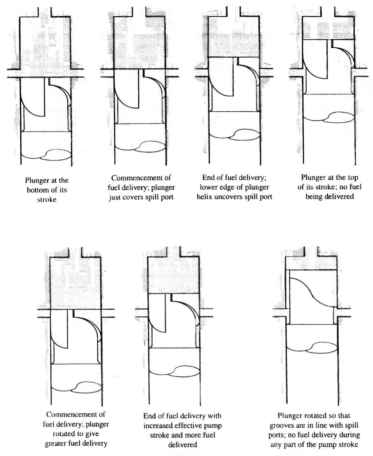

Plunger at the bottom of its stroke

Commencement of fuel delivery; plunger just covers spill port

End of fuel delivery; lower edge of plunger helix uncovers spill port

Plunger at the top of its stroke; no fuel being delivered

Commencement of fuel delivery; plunger rotated to give greater fuel delivery

End of fuel delivery with increased effective pump stroke and more fuel delivered

Plunger rotated so that grooves are in line with spill ports; no fuel delivery during any part of the pump stroke

Figure 40. Fuel Pump Operation with Helical Control

Variable Injection Timing Fuel Pump

With a flat topped plunger delivery of fuel commences at the same point in the plunger stroke, and consequently at the same camshaft and crankshaft angular position, in all cases. This is satisfactory in most cases, but there are times when changing the timing of fuel injection commencement has advantages. Engine operating efficiency is greatest when peak pressure and ignition temperature are maintained at their maximum permissible values. The load on gudgeon pin and large end bearings limit the value of peak pressure and a high maximum temperature can result in high levels of oxides of nitrogen emissions (NO_x). Advancing the injection timing at slightly reduced loads (between about 90 per cent and 100 per cent of Maximum Continuous Rating (mcr) enables peak pressure to be held virtually constant, keeping operating efficiency at a high level. This is achieved by raising the control edge of the pump plunger in these regions so that the spill port is covered earlier in the plunger stroke and injection commences earlier. At very low loads there might be insufficient energy in the exhaust gas to drive the turbocharger effectively, resulting in a reduction in air supply and consequent combustion problems. Retarding the injection timing at very low loads reduces cylinder efficiency but allows sufficient energy to be available in the exhaust gas to enable the turbocharger to provide the correct quantity of air, without the need for auxiliary blowers. Lowering the control edge on the plunger top delays the covering of the spill port which delays or retards the commencement of fuel injection **(Figure 41)**.

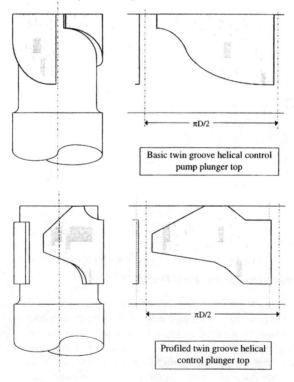

Basic twin groove helical control pump plunger top

Profiled twin groove helical control plunger top

Figure 41. Twin Groove Helical Control Plunger Tops

Plunger Adjustment

This may also be achieved by fitting a balancer device between the pump plunger and the cam. This is essentially the cam follower on its own rocker arm which has a moveable pivot point. Rotation of the eccentric shaft changes the position of the pivot point which effectively raises or lowers the pump plunger for a given camshaft position, thereby altering the commencement of fuel injection. Fuel quantity adjustment is achieved by means of the fuel rack causing rotation of the plunger. Another alternative is rotation of the cam and camshaft relative to the crankshaft as mentioned in Separate Forged Cams above **(Figure 42)**.

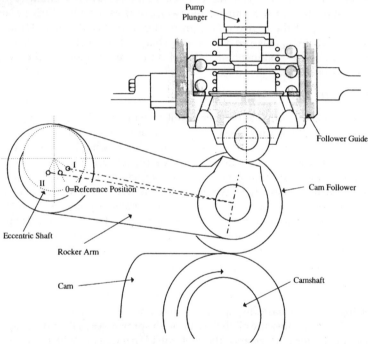

Figure 42. Balancer Mechanism for Adjustment of Fuel Pump Injection Timing

Injection Timing Adjustment

Adjustments to injection timing can be made by raising or lowering the plunger relative to the spill port. In most cases this is accomplished by fitting or removing shims which are located between the plunger foot and the tappet. In service the sharp edges of the spill port, the plunger top and the helix, tend to erode, which changes the timing and quantity of fuel injected at any rack setting. Correction for quantity may be made by adjusting the screwed linkage connecting the control rack to the fuel adjustment linkage, but timing correction can only be made by raising the plunger so its top covers the spill port at the correct time. This is usually accomplished by means of shims between the plunger foot and tappet.

Fuel Pump Cam Box Lubrication

Fuel pump barrels are completely isolated from the camshaft drive to prevent contamination of the cam box lubricating oil by fuel leaking past the plunger. Some pumps (e.g. those fitted to Sulzer ZA50S engines) have forced lubrication of the plunger by means of pressure oil which prevents fuel leakage past the plunger. Foreign matter in fuel causes barrel/plunger wear, as well as damage to valves and sharp edges on the spill port and plunger. Effective treatment of the fuel and care of filters in the system minimises problems.

Fuel Pump Delivery Valve

A delivery valve is fitted at the HP fuel oil outlet from the pump and plays an important role in ensuring effective operation of the injector. This acts as a non return valve, preventing fuel in the HP pipe from flowing back to the pump. The injector needle valve should close sharply, ensuring an abrupt end to injection without dribbling or secondary injection. The delivery valve is designed with a relatively large volume piston in its lower section and when the valve closes this piston is displaced from the delivery side of the pipe to a position below the seat area. Removal of such a large volume from the delivery side results in a rapid drop in pressure in the delivery pipe as the remaining oil must expand to occupy that space. The rapid fall in pressure closes the needle valve, abruptly ending injection.

Fuel Injector

Fuel injectors are basically spring loaded non-return valves which, when open, allow high pressure oil to flow through spray holes in the nozzle tip. For efficient cylinder performance the fuel must burn quickly which means that fuel droplets of about 10-15mm diameter must be produced during injection. Droplet size is a function of spray hole diameter and fuel pressure, which influences the velocity of the oil passing through the holes. Very fine droplets burn quickly as they have a large surface area per unit mass so the oxygen can readily reach the hydrocarbon molecules, which can only be done at the surface of the fuel droplet, however, fine droplets do not penetrate readily into the compressed air in the combustion chamber and do not mix with the available oxygen, so combustion can be impaired. Large droplets penetrate, but burn slowly because of the relatively small surface area per unit mass of fuel. Penetration can be too good and unburnt fuel droplets may impinge on the liner and piston crown surfaces. Large droplets can also cause afterburning which can damage exhaust valves. Optimum size is, therefore, a compromise but the size will tend towards fine droplets if the air in the combustion chamber is encouraged to swirl, encouraging the fuel and air to mix. Swirl is promoted by the piston crown shape in four stroke engines, and by the piston crown shape and port design in two stroke engines.

Injector Nozzle

Most engines employ a centrally fitted injector with a nozzle tip that its be provided with a number of spray holes. The disposition of the holes allows the production of a droplet spray pattern to suit the shape of the combustion chamber. Droplets should not impinge on the piston crown, cylinder head or liner, as this not only reduces performance but may cause local burning of these parts. Unburnt fuel may then be scraped off the liner into the crankcase where it will contaminate the lubricating oil. In addition, a defective fuel injector may cause poor engine emissions. Nozzle spray holes tend to erode during service, and this enlargement causes a change in droplet size and possibly in spray pattern. Injectors need to be removed from the cylinder at regular intervals, e.g. MAN-B&W L58/64 engines after 2-3,000 hours. Hole size is checked by inserting a Go/No-Go gauge. If the No-Go gauge will fit, the holes are too large and the nozzle must be replaced. This method is fine if holes erode in a truly circular shape but in many cases they do not, therefore, care must be taken when judging the size of a spray hole which has worn in a non-circular shape.

Fuel Atomisation

High pressure fuel enters the body of the injector via a filter unit, then flows down a hole drilled in the body to the needle valve unit. A vent valve is fitted in order to allow air to be removed from the system. At the nozzle tip the high pressure acts on the annular face of the needle valve, which is immediately below the guided portion of the valve. When fuel pressure has increased sufficiently to overcome the spring loading on the needle valve assembly, the needle valve will lift and high pressure fuel can flow through the nozzle holes. As the needle lifts, the lower tip of the valve is exposed to high pressure fuel so the valve immediately lifts to its fully open position, which allows full fuel flow to the spray holes. Full lift is very small – only a few millimetres – as the seat diameter of the valve is also only small. A valve's lifting pressure is set by an adjusting screw which acts on the setting spring (lifting pressure is in the region of 200 bar for most engines). At normal loads pressure in the fuel pipe will rise much higher than the lifting pressure and it is this maximum pressure which governs the fuel droplet size. Maximum pressures of 1500-2000 bar may be encountered in highly rated engine fuel pipes. Overheating of the fuel at the nozzle tip can result in pre-ignition of the fuel, leading to burning of the nozzle tip or the formation of carbon trumpets which destroy the spray pattern. Cooling of the injector is employed to restrict the temperature at the tip of the nozzle. This is often achieved by simply placing the injector in a water cooled pocket in the head but some engines, particularly those operating on residual fuel, are fitted with injectors which are cooled by circulating lubricating oil through drilled passageways in the body and nozzle tip **(Figure 43)**.

Fuel Ignition Delay

Fuel does not ignite as soon as it is injected. There is an ignition delay period while the combustion process is initiated and it takes some time for a flame to appear and for pressure to increase in the cylinder. The duration of this ignition delay depends on the ignition quality of the fuel being burned. Ignition quality relates to the Calculated Carbon Aromaticity Index (CCAI) of the fuel; the higher the CCAI, the longer the ignition delay. Fuel is still being injected during the delay period, and as soon as the flame appears all fuel in the cylinder will burn at once resulting in a very high peak pressure which could damage bearing surfaces. This is a problem for high powered engines with high rates of fuel injection, which operate on residual fuels. Later injection of the fuel is not an option as the ignition delay period would still be the same therefore the effect would be to reduce power, possibly leading to afterburning. A two stage or pilot injection system can avoid the problems of high injection rates with poor ignition quality fuels. The Wärtsilä Vasa 46 engine, for example, is provided with a pilot injection system employing a single fuel pump. Each cylinder has two injectors. The main injector is placed in the centre of the cylinder head and the pilot injector to one side. The pilot injector is designed to give the required droplet size and spray pattern at a lower fuel pressure than the main injector. It is also set to lift at a lower pressure. When the fuel pump pressure rises, the pilot injector will lift first, at the correct crank angle timing for effective combustion. At the ignition point of the fuel there is only a small quantity of fuel in the cylinder, which will burn, but the cylinder pressure rise will be limited. The main injector is set to open close to piston top dead centre (TDC) and when this happens the main fuel charge is injected; this will burn immediately because of the pilot flame provided by the pilot injection. The rise in cylinder pressure and temperature will be reasonable but the full charge of fuel can be injected without the risk of afterburning or high loads on bearings. This system has the added advantage of a lower peak temperature than with single stage injection, which restricts the formation of NO_x **(Figure 44)**.

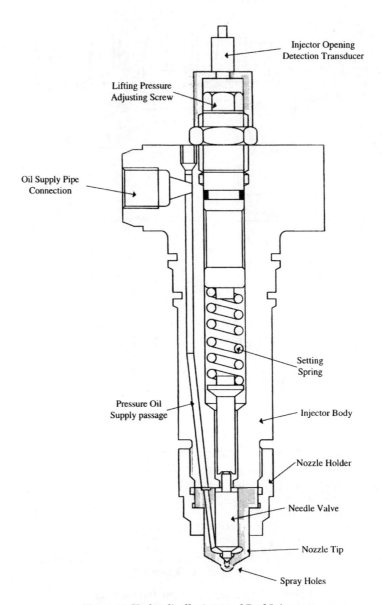

Injector Opening
Detection Transducer

Lifting Pressure
Adjusting Screw

Oil Supply Pipe
Connection

Setting
Spring

Pressure Oil
Supply passage

Injector Body

Nozzle Holder

Needle Valve

Nozzle Tip

Spray Holes

Figure 43. Hydraulically Actuated Fuel Injector

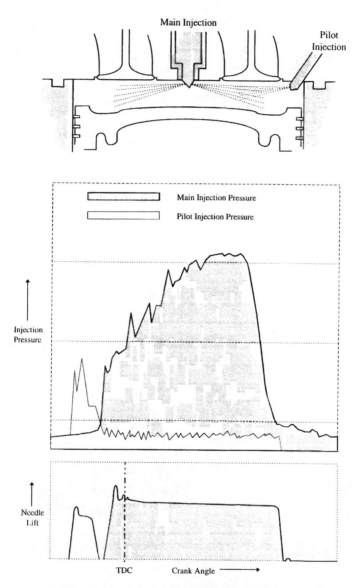

**Figure 44. Pilot Injection System (Wärtsilä Vasa 46)
(Injection Pressure Variation and Needle Valve Lift)**

2.7   ENGINE GOVERNOR

Compensation and Isochronous Governor

A governor maintains the engine speed at the desired value no matter how much load is applied. It achieves this by adjustment of the fuel pump racks. Any change in load will produce a change in engine speed, which will cause the governor to initiate a fuel change. The governor is said to be speed sensing as a speed change has to take place before the governor can react to adjust the fuel setting. The simple mechanical governor employs rotating weights which move outward as the speed increases and inward as the speed reduces; this movement, acting through a system of linkages, can be used to regulate the fuel rack. Rather than having the rotating weights directly move the fuel linkage, hydraulic governors employ a servo system so the rotating weights only need to move a pilot valve in the hydraulic line. This makes the governor more responsive. Governors of this type require a speed change to take place in order that they may initiate fuel rack adjustment. This is known as speed droop and there is a definite speed for each load therefore the governor cannot control to a single speed. A modification to the governor hydraulic system introduces a facility known as compensation which allows for further fuel adjustment after the main adjustment has taken place due to speed droop. Compensation restores the speed to its original desired value so the engine can operate at the same speed under all loads. Such a governor is said to be isochronous as the engine operates at a single speed. However, the governor is still speed sensing and so is not ideal for all applications.

Speed Sensing Governor

Where the engine drives an alternator any speed change results in a change in supply frequency. Large changes in electrical supply frequency can have an adverse effect on sensitive electronic equipment connected to that supply. Where electrical generation is involved it is possible to monitor the electrical load and use this as a means for actuating the governor response, rather than simply taking rotational speed as the control signal. Such governors is known as load sensing. It is extremely difficult to make a mechanical governor load sensing, even with a hydraulic system, but an electronic governor can take account of the electrical load applied to the engine and so can be considered 'speed sensing'.

Electronic Governor

Electronic governors essentially comprise two parts, the digital control unit and the hydraulic actuator, which are interlinked but it is useful to consider them separately.

Electronic Governor Controller

The digital control may be considered as a 'black box' in which signals are processed to produce a control signal which is sent to the actuator. The controller may be programmed in order to set points and parameters. The controller is a sensitive piece of electronic equipment and should not be mounted on the engine or in areas where it will be exposed to vibration, humidity or high temperatures. It should be ventilated in order to keep it cool and should be shielded from high-voltage or high-current devices which will cause electromagnetic interference. Similar restrictions apply to the location of signal cables. Speed signals are taken from two speed transducers, one on each side of the flexible coupling which attaches the engine to the load. Failure of one transducer produces a minor alarm but allows continued operation whenever possible. Failure of both speed transducers initiates an engine shutdown. An electronic overspeed value may be programmed into the controller in which case detection of overspeed will cause the engine to be shut off. If the load is provided by an electrical machine the output from that machine provides a signal for load sharing. Should this transducer fail the load on the engine will be determined by the position of the governor actuator output. The controller can also receive signals from other transducers including the engine's air inlet pressure, which allows the fuel to be limited when starting. After processing input signals in accordance with programmed requirements an output signal will be sent to the governor actuator **(Figure 45)**.

Electronic Governor Actuator

The actuator is a hydraulic device which moves the fuel linkage in response to a signal from the digital controller. The operating mechanism is contained within an oil filled casing. Oil pressure is provided by a geromotor pump driven by a shaft connected to the engine camshaft. At the heart of the actuator is the torque motor beam, which is balanced when the engine is operating at the desired speed. **(Figure 46)**.

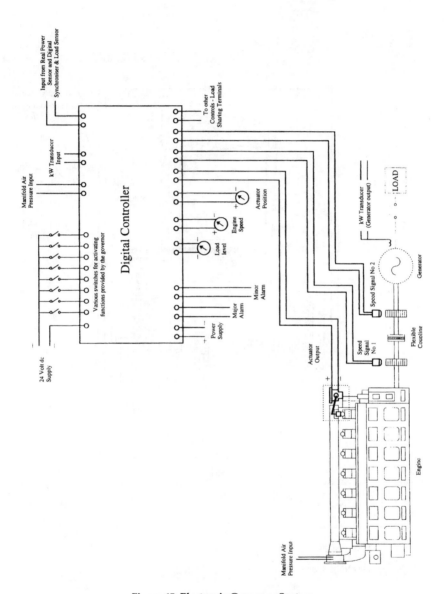

Figure 45. Electronic Governor System

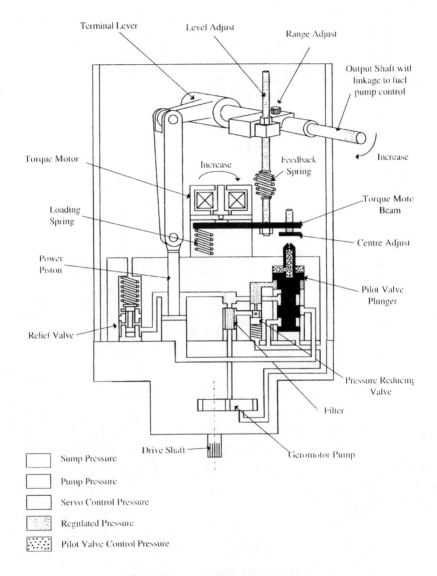

Terminal Lever   Level Adjust   Range Adjust

Output Shaft with
linkage to fuel
pump control

Torque Motor

Increase

Increase

Feedback
Spring

Loading
Spring

Torque Motor
Beam

Centre Adjust

Power
Piston

Pilot Valve
Plunger

Relief Valve

Pressure Reducing
Valve

Filter

Drive Shaft

Geromotor Pump

Sump Pressure

Pump Pressure

Servo Control Pressure

Regulated Pressure

Pilot Valve Control Pressure

Figure 46. Hydraulic Governor Actuation

a. Consider a load increase.

The controller increases current to the torque motor which, in turn, causes the centre adjust end of the torque motor beam to be lowered. Oil flow through the nozzle is reduced, which increases pressure on the top of the pilot valve plunger. This moves downward, uncovering the port which allows pressure oil to the lower face of the power piston, which in turn moves upwards, rotating the terminal shaft thereby increasing the fuel to the engine. As the terminal shaft rotates the torque motor beam is pulled upwards by increased tension in the feedback spring, increasing the clearance between the centre adjust and the nozzle. Leakage past the nozzle increases, reducing the pressure on the upper face of the pilot valve plunger and allowing the pilot valve to move upwards. This cuts off further oil to the power piston, and movement of the fuel control linkage ceases. Balance is restored to the torque motor beam with downward force from the feedback spring being matched by upwards force from oil leakage from the nozzle. The engine then operates at an increased fuel setting which matches the new load requirement at the set speed.

b. Consider a load reduction.

A decrease in load produces a reduction in current acting on the torque motor, which tends to turn the beam in an anti-clockwise direction about the torque motor pivot, resulting in an increased clearance between the centre adjust and the nozzle. Pressure reduces on the upper face of the pilot vale plunger and the pilot valve moves upwards, allowing the lower face of the power piston to connect with the geromotor pump suction. The power piston moves downwards, rotating the terminal shaft which reduces fuel to the engine and tension in the feedback spring. The centre adjust end of the torque motor beam is forced down, thereby reducing clearance between the centre adjust and the nozzle. Leakage past the nozzle reduces, pressure on the upper face of the pilot valve increases and the pilot valve moves upwards, shutting off the connection between the lower face of the power piston and pump suction. The engine now operates with reduced load and reduced fuel, but at the same original speed.

Actuator Oil

It is essential that the oil level in the actuator unit is maintained at the correct value and that only the appropriate grade of oil is used. Insufficient or contaminated oil can result in wear or seizure of the components. Oil should be tested at the intervals suggested by the supplier and must be replaced if its properties fall outside acceptable limits.

Actuator Linkages

Linkages from the actuator to the fuel regulating shaft must be correctly connected. They must also be of the required length and be locked in position to prevent them becoming detached. Full travel of the linkage must exceed the maximum travel of the engine fuel control to ensure that the engine fuel control is capable of moving from the 'off' position to 'full fuel'. Linkage ends must be provided with bearings which can withstand constant movement without wear, as such wear causes lost motion and subsequent maloperation of the control.

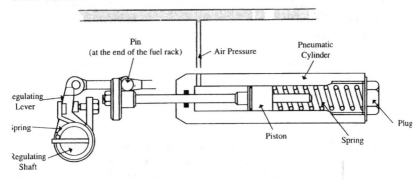

Figure 47. Overspeed Trip

Engine Overspeed Trip

An overspeed trip **(Figure 47)** is required to ensure the fuel supply will be removed from an engine should its speed exceed a predetermined value. Any overspeed device requires manual resetting. It should not be able to automatically reset after speed is reduced as the reason for overspeeding may still exist and the engine will race again. Overspeeding results if the engine load is suddenly removed by, for example, failure of a clutch or fracture of an alternator drive shaft. It is unusual for overspeeding to occur due to governor failure as fuel linkages are normally arranged so that failure in any part of the governor system results in fuel being shut off. Some engines are fitted with two independent overspeed devices, an electro-pneumatic device with a tripping speed set about 15 per cent above the nominal speed and a mechanical device set to about 18 per cent above nominal speed. The electro-pneumatic device, as fitted to Wärtsilä engines, has spring loaded pneumatic cylinders at each fuel pump, and when tripping occurs each fuel pump rack is moved to the 'no-fuel' position. During normal operation the spring force keeps the operating end of the rod clear of the pin at the end of the fuel rack, which can therefore be moved to any fuel position. Should overspeed occur a solenoid valve is actuated which allows air into the cylinder to act on the piston, moving it against the spring force. This causes the operating end of the piston rod to pull the pin on the end of the fuel rack fully over, shutting off fuel completely. A simple mechanical device may have a spring loaded button set into the rotating camshaft; when the speed exceeds a certain value, centrifugal force causes the button to move outward against the spring and actuate a system of levers which will move the fuel regulating lever to the full-off position. Both overspeed devices can be tripped manually if required.

Governor Regulating Shaft

The regulating shaft, supported in bearings, runs the length of the engine and provides a single means by which all full pumps may be adjusted. Movement of the governor output shaft is transferred to the regulating shaft by means of a spring loaded rod. This arrangement allows the stop or limit functions to be transferred to the regulating shaft irrespective of the governor position. Vee type engines have two regulating shafts, each with its own governor connection. Each fuel pump has its own regulating lever which is connected to the quantity control rack, however, the regulating levers are driven by means of torsion springs, and not rigidly attached to the regulating shaft. This arrangement means that fuel pump racks may be moved to the 'no-fuel' position even if the rack on one pump is jammed. Similarly, fuel racks may be moved to the 'fuel-on' position even if one fuel pump rack has jammed in the 'no-fuel' position. When starting, a fuel limiter automatically limits the movement of the regulating shaft and thereby the amount of fuel which can be supplied to the engine. A pneumatic cylinder acts against the fuel limiter lever, restricting fuel supply until the engine has reached a stable running condition. A fixed mechanical shaft movement limiter is also available to allow a maximum fuel setting under normal operating circumstances. The stop lever on the end of the regulating shaft enables fuel to be shut off from the engine to bring it to a stop. When the stop lever is moved to stop the engine, a system of levers rotates the regulating shaft to its stop position, causing the regulating levers to move all fuel racks to the 'no-fuel' position **(Figure 48)**.

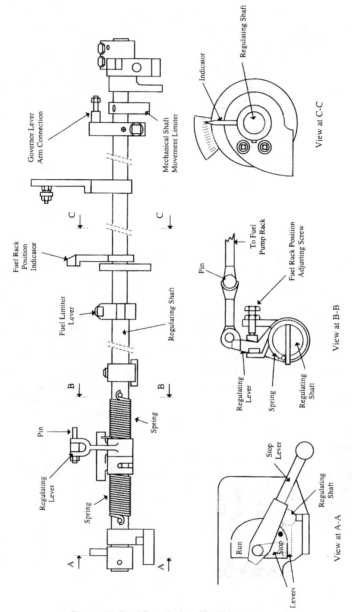

Figure 48. Fuel Regulating Shaft Arrangement

2.8   TURBOCHARGER SYSTEMS

Turbocharging

Turbocharging is a method by which energy in the cylinder exhaust gas is used to provide air for combustion. Four stroke cycle engines may operate in a normally aspirated mode, which means that the suction stroke of the piston draws air into the cylinder and so no pressurised air supply is necessary. A two stroke cycle engine requires air to be supplied at a pressure above atmospheric and so some means of providing that pressurised supply is necessary. A four stroke cycle engine can, therefore, operate without a pressurised combustion air supply but a two stroke cycle engine cannot. However, the operation of a pressure charged four-stoke engine under non-pressure charged, or normally aspirated conditions, is not advised as it is likely to result in severe fouling and possible thermal damage.

Supercharging

Supercharging, or pressure charging, means the supply of air to an engine at pressures higher than atmospheric in order to increase the air mass in the cylinder and so enable more fuel to be burned and more power to be developed. Such a system may be applied to four stroke and two stroke cycle engines. As with the supply of scavenge air, reciprocating pumps or chain driven blowers may be used, but such systems take power from the crankshaft. The use of exhaust gas blowers, or turbo-chargers, is more efficient. Compressing the air increases its temperature, which can have an adverse effect on the cylinder as higher temperature not only reduces the air density but also increases combustion temperature which can cause problems with the formation of NO_x (see Chapter 3). Consider the equation:

$$PV = mRT$$

Where:

P = Pressure (N/m^2)

V = Volume (m^3)

m = Mass (kg)

R = Gas Constant (J/kg.K.)

T = Absolute Temperature (K)

Air density in the cylinder is given by:

$$\frac{m}{V} = \frac{P}{RT}$$

However, as R is a constant the air density in the cylinder may be expressed as:

$$\frac{m}{V} = (f)\frac{P}{T}$$

i.e. the air density is a function of:

$$\frac{P}{T}$$

It follows that pressure must be increased in order to increase the air density, and that is the purpose of the turbocharger. As compression also tends to increase the air temperature, the density will not increase at the same rate as the pressure if temperature is not controlled. Doubling the pressure will not double the air density unless the air temperature is kept constant. Coolers are fitted in the air supply trunking between the turbocharger compressor outlet and the inlet to the engine, to control the combustion air density. Coolers may not be fitted in smaller engines, to simplify the system, but for medium speed engines employed for propulsion, air coolers enable higher cylinder powers to be achieved. This is because a greater air mass is supplied to the cylinder than would otherwise be the case, allowing more fuel to be burned and greater power to be developed. This is called supercharging.

Turbocharger

A turbocharger consists of two parts, the gas side which comprises the turbine and the air side which comprises the rotary compressor. Turbine disc and compressor impeller are mounted on the same shaft. For smaller units the rotor, which comprises two sections of shaft and a turbine disc, may be a single forging. For larger units the turbine disc is separate and the sections of shaft are attached by bolted flanges. Bearings support the rotor at its ends and the cast iron casing is water cooled. At the compressor end the casing is of aluminium alloy and is uncooled. Some engines may be fitted with what are known as 'uncooled' turbochargers. These are compact units with a bearing at the centre of the shaft, with the turbine disc and compressor impeller located at opposite ends of the rotor.

Turbocharger Arrangement

Although the design of turbochargers may differ the fundamental principles are the same for all models. It is the principles which will be considered here, together with the arrangements as they relate to medium speed engines.

A turbine consists of a single row of rotating blades mounted on a disc. Gas is directed onto the moving blades by an annular arrangement of nozzle blades. Moving blades fit axially into the disc using inverted fir-tree roots, or similar. Blade design, both moving and fixed, is critical to performance and varies according to the type of turbine system. Although the pulse system of turbocharging has been very popular for medium speed engines, and remains so, constant pressure systems are often employed where high powered engines are used for propulsion purposes. Vee type engines normally have separate turbochargers for each bank of cylinders.

Turbocharger, Pulse System

The pulse system makes use of the high pressure kinetic and thermal energy in the exhaust gas when the exhaust commences, and the timing of the exhaust is critical to turbocharger performance. Early opening of the exhaust was often employed as a means of obtaining sufficient exhaust gas energy. This system has proved popular as it enables the turbocharger to supply sufficient air for good combustion at all loads. The pulse system employs relatively small bore pipes connecting the cylinders to the turbocharger, to avoid a loss of gas energy in the exhaust piping. Exhaust gas flows from each cylinder for about 120°; to avoid interference between pulses, groups of three cylinders are generally connected to particular sections of turbocharger nozzle. This implies a multiple inlet arrangement for the turbine. A six-cylinder engine would require two turbocharger entries and a nine-cylinder engine, three entries, or two turbochargers. Pulse systems are ideally suited to engines where frequent and large changes in load take place, such as those used for electrical generation, but their exhaust gas piping systems can become complex particularly for engines with a large number of cylinders. Turbine and nozzle blades must be designed to cope efficiently with the wide range of gas pressures which exist over a cycle, which implies relatively thick blade sections with well rounded entry noses **(Figure 49)**.

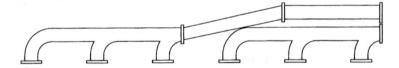

Pulse Turbo-Charging System with Twin Entry Blower

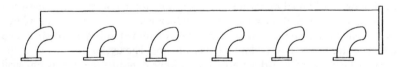

Constant Pressure Turbo-Charging System

Figure 49. Turbo-Charger Exhaust Manifold Systems

Turbocharger, Constant Pressure System

The constant pressure turbocharging system has all cylinders supplying exhaust gas to a large volume manifold, which then directs the gas to the turbocharger nozzle ring. Pulse or kinetic energy is not required, so exhaust can commence later in the piston stroke achieving a slight increase in cylinder power. Exhaust gas in the manifold is maintained at a relatively steady pressure, at any particular engine load, and so the turbine and nozzle blades can be designed to suit steady conditions. Blade sections tend to be thinner and have sharper noses than for pulse blading. Constant pressure systems do not react as quickly to sudden load changes, but they are more efficient and have a relatively simple exhaust pipe arrangement.

Turbocharger Compressor

The turbocharger turbine drives a rotary compressor which consists of an impeller and volute casing. Air enters the impeller at its centre or 'eye'; rotation of the impeller imparts a high velocity to the air which then moves outwards into the stationary diffuser and volute casing. This casing has a steadily increasing cross sectional area and is like an inverted nozzle wrapped around the impeller. The volute converts velocity energy into pressure energy, just as a nozzle converts pressure energy into velocity energy, and the air leaves the compressor casing at a relatively low velocity but at increased pressure. The impeller is basically a disc with a number of radial vanes which reduce in depth from the eye to the periphery. The rotor assembly, comprising turbine, shaft and impeller, is a balanced set but the impeller can be removed from the rotor. The impeller fits onto the rotor using a splined connection. In order to preserve balance the impeller is made so it will only fit onto the rotor in a particular position, usually by having one of the splines larger than the rest. A suction filter is provided before the eye of the impeller to remove dust and oil particles which could build up on the impeller, volute and cooler, reducing performance. The filter acts as a silencer but insulating felt on the suction manifold also reduces noise.

Intercooling

Air cooling is achieved by means of one or more intercoolers located between the impeller outlet and the air manifold, which runs the length of the engine. These coolers are comprised of a number of finned tubes through which cooling water flows, the air flowing over the fins. The use of fins increases the effective heat transfer surface area and allows a reduction in the physical external dimensions of the cooler. Provision must be made for thermal expansion of the tubes, generally by employing U-tubes which have in-built compensation for thermal expansion. Water inlet and outlet headers are then provided on the same side of the cooler making for more accessible pipe connections. In some cases water separators are fitted between the cooler and air trunking in order to remove any water droplets which might form during cooling of the combustion air. Water entering the cylinder can remove the oil film from the cylinder liner but this is more of a problem with two stroke cycle engines, where the air enters through ports in the lower part of the liner rather than valves in the cylinder head.

Turbochargers Matching to Engine

Highly rated high powered engines used for propulsion must be capable of meeting a wide range of loads. However, cylinder conditions must be kept within certain limits in terms of maximum pressure and temperature. In many cases turbochargers are matched to the engine so that they produce nominal full output at about 85 per cent of engine power. At higher loads the engine produces too much exhaust gas energy for the turbine. A waste gate is fitted in the exhaust manifold to the turbine so that some of the exhaust gas can be directed to the uptake rather than passing through the turbine. Similarly an air waste gate may be fitted to the air supply manifold to release excess combustion air pressure. Turbochargers fitted to engines have to deal with wide load ranges and they cannot be efficient at all loads. At high loads too much combustion air may be supplied, which can have an adverse effect on the engine. The use of exhaust gas and air waste gates enables the turbocharger(s) to provide high charge air pressures at low powers. This improves fuel consumption, produces a reduction in thermal loadings and allows for better response to load changes. Engines running at variable speed may be fitted with a charge air bypass which effectively puts some of the charge air into the exhaust gas trunking under certain operating conditions. The use of the charge air bypass permits the matching of valve overlap and turbocharger for best specific fuel oil consumption (SFOC) when the by-pass is closed, about 85 per cent of mcr, and avoids the risk of turbocharger surging at lower powers when the bypass is open. Depending on the engine design and operating conditions a charge air waste gate, exhaust waste gate and charge air bypass may be fitted. All devices are operated automatically by the engine's control system **(Figure 50)**.

Air Start Systems.

Compressed air is used for starting the engine. The starting air system operating at a pressure of about 30 bar. Minimum air pressure for starting is in the region of 12 bar (these values differ according to engine design).The capacity of the starting air receivers depends on the size of engine and needs to comply with Classification Society requirements which require a minimum 12 starts for reversing engines and 6 starts for non-reversing engines.

Figure 50. Turbocharge System Incorporating Charge Air Bypass and Charge Air Waste Gate

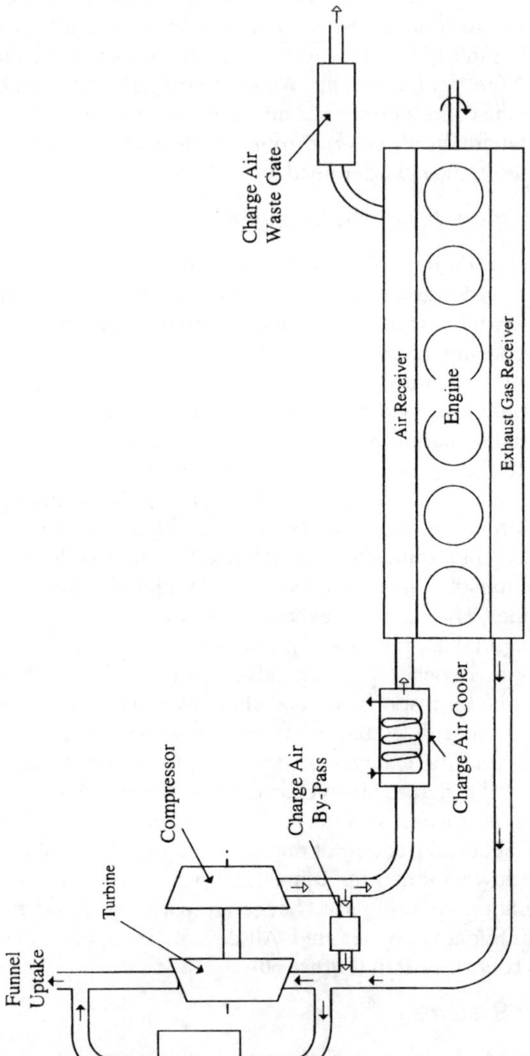

Starting Air System

Starting air valves are fitted in the cylinder heads of all cylinders except for Vee engines where it is normal to fit them in just one of the banks of cylinders. Each valve has a flame arrester fitted between the valve and the starting air manifold. Pilot air acting on a cylinder in the valve regulates opening and closing. This pilot air comes from a distributor rotated by the engine camshaft. A slow turning facility is provided for engines which have been at rest for a certain period of time, allowing the crankshaft to be turned two complete revolutions at reduced air pressure before full air pressure is applied. Successful completion of two revolutions on reduced air pressure means that all systems on a four stroke cycle engine will have operated including a test for hydraulic lock in the cylinders. In two stroke cycle engines a single revolution is required on slow turning. The starting system is linked with the fuel system, which restricts fuel supply on starting to keep speed within set limits before being run up to full operating speed. Fuel and starting air are never supplied to a cylinder at the same time due to the risk of explosion. Fuel is applied only when the engine has achieved the desired rotational speed and the air start valves are shut. A similar arrangement in the control system enables the engine to be shut down pneumatically (see Overspeed Trip, above). Local and remote starting is provided for most engines although certain small engines only have local starting. Depending on the type of installation a power management system may operate which will start and stop engines automatically depending on the load. Such systems apply to diesel electric propulsion where the prime movers provide power for propulsion and hotel loads **(Figure 51)**.

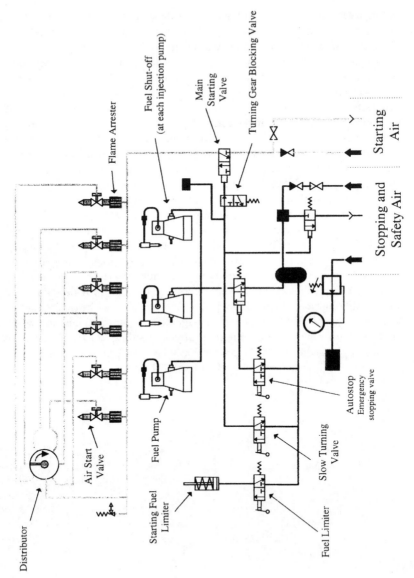

Figure 51. Starting Air System

2.9   ENGINE DRIVE PUMPS AND COOLERS

Lubricating Oil And Cooling Water Circulating Pumps

Lubricating oil and cooling water circulating pumps are driven from the crankshaft, although some large engines may employ external pumps. The drive for such pumps is located at the free end of the engine as this gives ease of access for overhaul. Engine driven pumps simplify the plant system design but take power from the crankshaft.

Lubricating Oil And Jacket Water Coolers

Coolers may be integral with the engine, separate for the particular engine system or a central cooling system may be employed. Whatever the arrangement cooling capacity must be sufficient to meet the maximum demands of the engine. Integral coolers are generally of the tubular type, with plain tubes connected to tube plates. One of the tube plates is allowed to float in order to accommodate thermal expansion. External coolers are normally of the plate type. Adequate sea water must be circulated in order to cool the fresh water and the lubricating oil and care must be taken to minimise the risk of sea water leakage which can cause corrosion (**Figures 52 and 53**).

Lubricating systems draw oil from the sump of the engine and circulate it to all bearings, the camshaft drive, cam boxes and rocker assemblies. Oil is also used as the piston coolant. A system of pipes is used to supply lubricant to all locations. Holes in the crankshaft and connecting rods direct the oil to the large and small end bearings as well as the piston cooling cavity. The lubricating oil pressure should be such that it ensures adequate pressure at all locations. A pressure of about 8 bar is sufficient for most installations. The quantity of oil depends on the size of the engine and the cooling loads of the pistons. Where engine driven pumps are employed it is necessary to pre-lubricate the engine before it is started so that sufficient oil film is present on all bearing surfaces. A pre-lubricating pump is installed for this purpose. Lubricating oil is circulated by positive displacement pumps of the screw or gear type, which ensures the lubricant will circulate whenever the pump operates. In general, cylinder lubrication is by means of splash from the crankcase, but some engines provide a positive supply via quill points in the cylinder liner wall. Such arrangements seem to give better control of cylinder oil supply, however effective scraper rings on the piston also work well. As oil circulates through the engine its temperature will rise so it is essential for a cooler to be fitted to limit temperature and subsequent thermal problems. Oxidation of the oil is the main result of high temperature which can give rise to loss of lubrication ability. Other problems which particularly affect trunk piston engines include fuel dilution, water contamination and carbon buildup, and the oil charge should be tested frequently to allow early detection of potential problems. Although shipboard test kits are available, it is considered the best practice to send samples to a shore based laboratory at frequent intervals. Turbocharger and governor oil systems are separate from the crankcase system and these should also be monitored. Filters in the oil circulating system remove small solid particles, however, manual cleaning or back flushing is required at intervals as suggested by the engine builder. Choice of lubricant is generally down to the engine operator although engine builders will often offer suggestions. The experience of the engine builder and operator, as well as the advice of the oil suppliers, should be used in making a decision on the grade of oil to be used. Availability of that grade worldwide should also be taken into account. Failure to comply with the engine builder's recommendations can void guarantees.

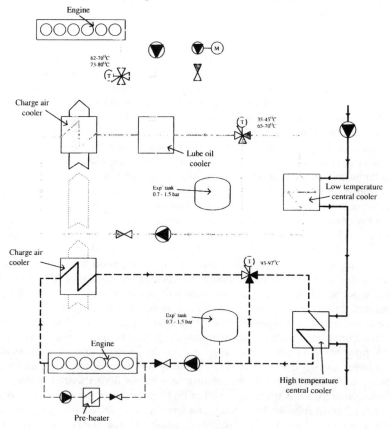

Figure 52. Central Cooling System Incorporating Arrangements for Jacket Water, Lube Oil and Charge Air Cooling

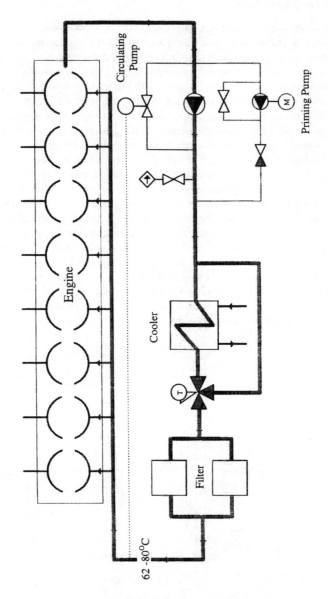

Figure 53. Engine Lubricating Oil Cooling System

Crankcase Explosion

Mineral oils are based on crude oil and so are a potential fire hazard. The avoidance of crankcase explosions is an important factor in engine design and operation. Hot spots, which can vaporise oil locally, can form where there is any metal-to-metal contact such as at bearings, gears, cylinder walls, etc. This vapour can circulate to a cooler part of the crankcase where it condenses to form droplets about 10mm diameter, which will burn readily. As the amount of mist increases the concentration of the mist/oxygen mixture will rise and eventually exceed the lower explosion limit. Should this mixture then come into contact with the hot spot an explosion will result. The severity of any such explosion depends on the actual amount of mist present. To prevent damage to the crankcase structure, spring loaded relief valves are fitted, to each unit for larger engines, which lift to release the pressure. Ingress of air back through the valve is prevented by immediate closing of the relief valve. An oil wetted gauze takes the heat out of the flame and a shield deflects the hot gases downwards. The vacuum which follows the explosion can draw fresh air into the crankcase through any available opening and the shock wave which proceeds the flame can break down mechanically produced oil droplets into fine mist like droplets. Should the hot spot persist a secondary much more severe explosion can result. Mist detectors are fitted on larger engines to give warning of the buildup of mist and some engines have various other means of detecting the presence of hot spots **(Figure 54)**.

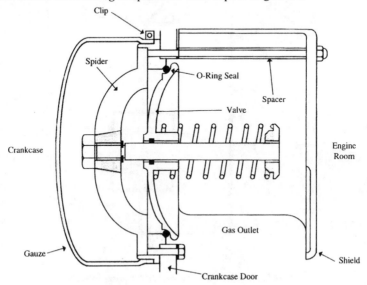

Figure 54. Crankcase Explosion Relief Door

Mineral Oil Additives

Mineral oils contain additives which give the required properties but synthetic oils are also available which are not as susceptible to deterioration. Synthetic oils are much more expensive than lubricants based on mineral oils, however, so they are only rarely used.

Engine Cooling Water

Cooling water must be treated to minimise the risk of corrosion in the cooling system, even if distilled water is used. Distilled water will prevent salt scale formation on the cooling surfaces but will not prevent corrosion. The most common corrosion cells are due to dissimilar metals and differential aeration. The use of effective corrosion inhibitors will minimise corrosion. The water should be tested at frequent intervals to ensure the inhibitor level is adequate, as a reduction in concentration can increase the risk of corrosion. For larger installations, particularly as part of a central cooling system, certain inhibitors such as chromates are not allowed if the jacket water is used as the heat source for low pressure evaporator plant producing fresh water for domestic purposes. Located in the cooling pipe system is a header tank, which is situated about 10 metres above the engine to ensure the cooling water system is maintained under pressure by the head of water. This tank may also act as a reserve in case of water leakage from the system or as an expansion tank to which overflow from the system may be directed. Flow in the engine cooling system is upward; water enters at the lowest part of the cylinder jacket and leaves at the highest part of the system, the cylinder heads or turbocharger outlets. This ensures that the water temperature gradually increases as it flows to the hottest parts of the system, but also means that any air will flow upwards and out of the system rather than forming air pockets which will impair circulation.

System Alarms

The jacket water and lubricating systems are protected by alarms for both pressure and temperature. System reaction depends on the alarm and the items included within the system. Temperature alarms will usually signal the engineer, while pressure reduction will either initiate the startup of a reserve pump – if separate pumps are employed – or engine shutdown if internal pumps are used.

Summary of Engine Construction

Engine Structure: Modern form is monoblock with underslung crankshaft for rigidity and strength. Nodular cast iron construction. Underslung crankshaft bearings mean no weight of running gear on upper shells.

Crankshaft:	Solid forged with large bearing surfaces and overlap between pins and journals for rigidity.
Bearing Shells:	Thin shell bearings for ease of maintenance, bi-metal bearings with overlay for corrosion resistance.
Connecting Rods:	Solid forged and sometimes split in order to allow lift of piston and connecting rod (conn-rod) with limited headroom requirement. Lubricant and cooling oil flow up hole in conn-rod.
Small end:	Stepped to provide effective bearings.
Large end:	Vee type engines with side-by-side, fork & blade or articulated arrangements to suit designer requirements.
Pistons:	Oil cooled with steel crown and cast iron skirt. Dished crown for shaped combustion chamber.
Piston Skirt:	Carries gudgeon pin and rubs against the liner. Essential for two stroke cycle engines.
Aluminium Piston:	Low weight, but low strength compared with steel; aluminium is alloyed to increase strength and thicker sections are used than with steel pistons. Solid with cast-in cooling coil.
Rotating Piston:	Even loading on piston and even distortion allowing for reduced piston-to-liner clearance; reduction in cylinder lubrication and risk of blowpast.
Piston Rings:	Clearances in piston and liner are critical to performance. Contoured and coated rings for wear and running-in. Oil scraper rings needed to control cylinder lubrication. Nodular cast-iron with chrome facings.
Cylinder Liner:	Nodular cast-iron with thick upper section for strength. Bore cooled in upper section.
Anti-polishing Ring:	Fitted in upper part of liner to reduce liner polishing and cylinder oil consumption.
Cylinder Heads:	Water cooled cast construction, sometimes bore cooled.

Cylinder Cooling: Thick sections cause problems of thermal stress but are needed for mechanical strength. Bore cooling provides solution to high thermal loads and high cylinder peak pressures.

Exhaust Valves: Caged valves for ease of maintenance; valve rotation for wear and corrosion reduction; rotocaps and spinners; hydraulic operation of valves. Coatings on seats for long life.

Double Valves: Large surface area to reduce pumping losses and give full charge of air in cylinder. Rocker arrangements for double valves.

Camshaft: Cams forged separately and hydraulically 'shrunk on' or forged as part of camshaft. Camshaft gear drive system and retiming by rotation relative to crankshaft.

Fuel Pumps: Of the helical control type with profiled plunger to allow for variation in injection timing. Two stage injection systems for high CCAI fuels and for control of NO_x.

Fuel Injectors: Critical fuel spray pattern and droplet size; control of droplet size important hence need for testing and maintenance.

Governor: Speed control using an electronic governor which has inputs from a number of engine areas; rapid response to load changes possible. Hydraulic actuator for moving fuel linkage.

Overspeed Trip: Required as safeguard; acts on the fuel regulating shaft or on individual fuel pumps in some engines.

Regulating Shaft: Linkages allow shaft to be moved even though one fuel pump may be stuck.

Turbochargers: Pulse and constant pressure systems available. Systems differ in terms of turbocharger design, exhaust timing, piping and efficiency. Pulse system responds quickly to rapid and large load variations but constant pressure more efficient.

Supercharging: Increased air supply to the engine allows more fuel to be burned and more power developed.

Air Cooling: Use of coolers allows for increased air density and greater mass available in cylinder for combustion. Cooling keeps cylinder temperatures reasonable.

Air Start: Engines started with compressed air. Vee engines only have air start valves on one bank of cylinders.

Pumps: Small engines may have engine driven pumps while large engines generally have external pumps.

Coolers: Lubricating oil and jacket water coolers are provided to limit temperatures; large systems may employ a central cooling arrangement for simplicity and to reduce the amount of pipework and number of coolers in contact with seawater.

3   Engine Choice and Installation

Engine Choice

The choice of engine for a particular application depends on a number of factors, including personal preference. If an owner already has a number of engines from a particular manufacturer in his fleet then the operators will already be familiar with the operation and maintenance of that manufacturer's engines. Availability of spares should also be considered, as should the quality of backup services available, particularly if the engine is to operate in a remote region away from the engine builder's base. Owners are concerned about the cost of engine operation, and the operating period between the replacement of major components must be taken into account, as must the manpower requirements for overhaul. Although the cost of spares is quantifiable, most of the other factors mentioned above are not, at least not directly, but must still be taken into account. Choice of engine is dictated by power and speed requirements; a builder's layout diagram may be used to make the selection from a range of engines. Not all combinations of speed and power will be covered and the final choice is always something of a compromise **(Figure 55)**.

Specific Fuel Consumption

Specific Fuel Consumption (SFC), the amount of fuel needed to generate a unit of power, is important, as fuel is the major operating cost of the engine. Engines offered by major builders in particular power ranges are competitive as far as SFC is concerned. Brake Specific Fuel Consumption figures of around 175 g/kWh are typical. Lubricating oil consumption must also be taken into account as this also relates to the power developed. An overall consumption of about 1.0 g/kWh can be expected from most large medium speed engines. Such figures, obviously, relate to the power developed by the engine, and most builders aim to have minimum SFC at around 85 per cent of mcr. Ideally the engine will operate at or about 85 per cent of mcr to keep fuel consumption reasonable. In most cases an installation will consist of a number of engines, whether used for electrical generation or propulsion, and engines will be loaded to about 85 per cent mcr before other engines are started **(Figure 56)**.

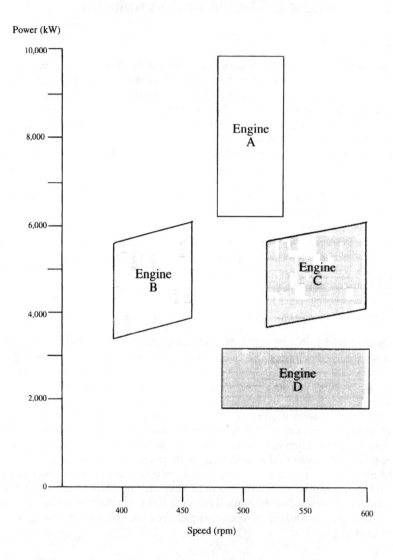

Figure 55. Layout Diagram for an Engine Range Showing Power and Speed Combinations Covered

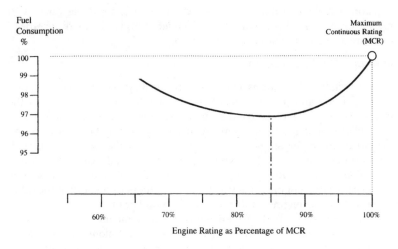

Figure 56. Diagram Showing Relationship between Fuel Consumption and Developed Power

Space Considerations

Flexibility is the keyword to any engine installation. Engines must occupy as little space as possible within the ship, especially if such space could be used for cargo or passengers. Medium speed engines are of low height compared with crosshead engines, making them ideal for passenger ships and vehicular ferries – although a medium speed installation can be applied to any type of ship. Certainly tugs, offshore supply vessels and similar small tonnage vessels find medium speed engines ideal for the limited space available. The limited space available in the hull compartments of catamaran craft means that the medium speed engine is the only option, apart from gas turbines. For electrical generation, engines may be arranged in the hull in any convenient manner and need not to be arranged in a fore and aft manner. However, gear driven systems for propulsion do need to have engines arranged in line with the propeller shaft and, in general, on the same plane.

Speed Range and Power Requirements

Large vessels such as cruise liners have to operate at a wide range of speeds to suit schedules. Power requirements will therefore vary but, ideally, the engines should operate at around 85 per cent of mcr in order to minimise fuel consumption. Engine builders offer engines in ranges which cover both speed and power. Not all power and speed combinations will be available, and a compromise may be required if a particular type and cylinder size is required.

Propulsion installations may be geared drive with controllable pitch (CP) propeller or electric drive with CP propeller. Reversible medium speed engines are available but are very rarely used.

'Father and Son' Installation

A geared installation requires clutches between engines and gearbox and between gearbox and propeller shaft. The gear ratio must be such that the engine speed (say 500 to 600 rpm) may be reduced to an acceptable value at the propeller (about 150 to 200 rpm). A single engine may be used for small installations. In larger ships a multiple engine installation is used, with engines arranged side-by-side to keep engine room length reasonable. Many large geared diesel drives employ the 'father and son' style of installation. This consists of two engines, one (the 'father') of higher power than the other (the 'son'). As these engines differ only in the number of cylinders, the same spares can be used in both. At low power requirements the 'son' engine operates up to its mcr. For further increase the 'father' alone operates to its mcr; at full power requirement both engines operate. This arrangement allows flexible operation and enables engines to operate close to a fuel efficient mcr of 85 per cent. Additional engines are needed to generate electrical power for hotel services but it is possible to include alternators in the system. These can be driven from the gearbox or as power take off units from any or all engines. In many cases CP propeller drives do not run at constant speed. The drive speed and propeller pitch will vary over a particular load range when manoeuvring. In such cases it is necessary to ensure alternator drives run at constant speed to maintain frequency.

Diesel Electric Propulsion

The diesel electric installation is considered to be the most flexible for large passenger ship installations, although diesel electric propulsion itself is not as efficient as a gear driven system. A number of engines are employed to drive high voltage alternators. The power is directed to the propulsion motors and is also used, via transformers, to meet the ship's hotel loads. A computer controlled power management system is generally used to start and stop engines in response to load changes.

Maintenance and Headroom

It has already been mentioned that the low height of the in-line or Vee type medium speed diesel engine makes it ideal for passenger ships and vehicular ferries. Headroom must also be available for maintenance. The lifting of pistons, cylinder heads and liners requires space above the engine. The use of split connecting rods means that only a short piece of connecting rod remains attached to the piston when it is lifted, and this reduces the headroom requirement for overhaul. (see 'Connecting Rods' in Chapter 2.)

Load Diagrams

Engine builders provide load diagrams for their engines. These show how the engine can be matched to the propeller and loaded over its range. Load diagrams relate to particular engines and propeller systems, e.g. CP or fixed pitch (FP). Each builder has their own way of presenting the information, so load diagrams differ from engine to engine. If the prime mover operates at a constant speed, the diagram will differ from one in which the engine has a range of operating speeds. Similarly, the diagram for an engine driving a CP propeller will differ slightly from that for the same engine arranged to power a constant speed alternator system. The load diagrams shown are based on those devised by Sulzer for its 'Z' range of engines and are used for illustrative purposes only. For a specific engine, actual values would be given for engine speed and engine power.

CP Propellers

Although it is possible to drive a CP propeller at constant speed it is usual practice to operate at reduced speed at lower power, so the propeller pitch and speed are varied together. A load-up (and load-down) profile of speed and power is arranged below 45 per cent load in figure 57. The area A represents the range in which the engine can be operated and the area B represents the area in which the engine may operate for short periods. Area C represents the permitted overspeed operating range and D1, the optimum operating area for clean hull and good weather. The range D1 indicates a lower power requirement than the maximum allowed for the engine. Note that as the hull becomes fouled or weather conditions deteriorate there will be an increased power requirement for the same ship speed. This ideal range, D1, is below the nominal propeller characteristic line. The upper limit of the maximum operating range, B, is defined by the constant mep line (mep = constant), and constant mep is maintained down to about 95 per cent maximum engine rating to ensure maximum fuel economy. The full speed maximum continuous power is defined by the contract maximum continuous rating (CMCR). Below this point, the upper limit of the B region is defined by steadily reducing mep to restrict mechanical loading in the cylinders. Below about 64 per cent maximum power, the upper limit of operation is defined by the thermal loading consideration (Economic Rating or Maximum Continuous Rating). In practice the engine never operates near these lines but will stay within the region defined by D1 **(Figure 57)**.

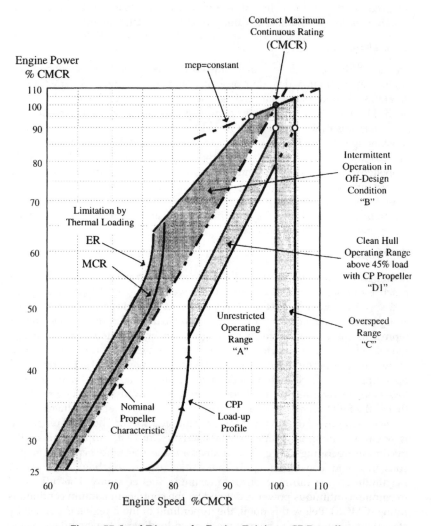

Figure 57. Load Diagram for Engine Driving a CP Propeller

Constant Speed Operation

In an engine designed for constant speed operation, e.g. an alternator drive, the load diagram is only concerned with the constant operating speed given by line D2 and the permitted overspeed range C. The load diagram has restricted operating areas as defined by A and B, but these are academic for constant speed control, provided the governor can regulate the system to give such constant speed. Because engine speed remains constant at all operating loads, there can be operational problems where sudden power changes occur. The combustion air produced by the turbocharger may not match with engine requirements and so a waste gate for exhaust gas and/or manifold air may be required. A manifold air pressure limiter and a torque limiter may also be required depending on the size and type of the installation. Additional operational graphs should be considered when designing the plant **(Figure 58)**.

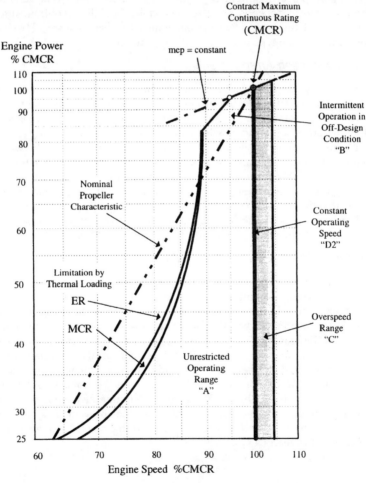

Figure 58. Load Diagram for Constant Speed Operation of Engine

Other Factors in System Design

A system may, in theory, be designed from the information in load diagrams. However, many other factors need to be considered, including the exhaust gas flow from the engine and exhaust gas temperature. The engine builder will provide such information for mcr operation and Economic Rating (ER) operation. This allows turbocharger and exhaust systems to be designed **(Figure 59)**.

Figure 59 shows that the selection of machinery is not just a matter of deciding on power requirements. Many other factors have to be considered. The final choice depends on space available, flexibility requirements, fuel economy and the propulsion system which has been chosen. There is no single ideal engine type or size to suit any situation.

Engine Mounting Arrangements

Engines must be firmly located in the ship; this requires some form of mounting arrangement. Where an engine is part of an electricity generating set, it is often the case that engine and electrical machine are mounted together on a foundation unit. The raft on which both sit is then fixed in the ship as a single unit. This arrangement ensures that alignment is maintained between the engine output shaft and alternator shaft. For larger electrical installations, such as those for diesel electric propulsion plants, and for geared diesel propulsion systems, the engines are mounted separately in the ship. Steps must be taken to ensure that the engine is correctly aligned with other connected items of plant, such as the gearbox. The foundation within the ship should be as rigid as possible in all directions so that all dynamic forces are absorbed.

Loading from Engine Forces and Moments

The nature, extent and cause of dynamic forces and moments due to the engines is a complex matter which is beyond the scope of the current work. However, engine builders will provide details of all forces and moments (couples) so action can be taken to ensure the mounting arrangements can withstand the loading. In a correctly balanced engine, vertical forces should be at a minimum (see 'Crankshaft and Main Bearings' in Chapter 2) but operation of the engine will cause additional moments. These include twisting about the axis of the crankshaft, about the vertical axis and about the transverse axis of the engine. The engine mounting arrangements must be able to withstand these forces as well as counter movement of the engine when the ship rolls and pitches. Thrust arrangements will generally be included in the gearbox system.

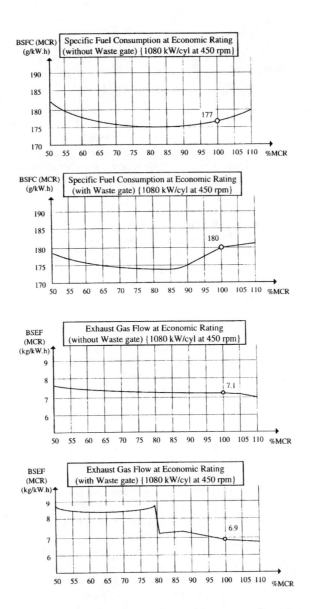

Figure 59. Typical Information Provided by Engine Builders relating to Fuel Consumption and Exhaust Gas Flows at Different Engine Loads

Engine Mounting

An engine can be fixed in a ship using a rigid or a flexible mounting.

Rigid Mountings

Rigid mountings consist of studs which extend from the lower face of the foundation plate to the upper face of the bedplate. Steel or non-metallic (resins) chocks are located between the bedplate and foundation plate. Chocks should be thick enough to ensure correct alignment between the engine shaft and the connecting shaft systems. Holding down studs are hydraulically tightened to ensure correct tension. This tension is dependent on the material used in the chock. Chocking must comply with Classification Society rules. Special requirements govern the fitting and conditions of use of non-metallic chocking. A maximum temperature limit of about 75°C applies with many resins. Side supports are fitted with both steel and resin chocks. These supports absorb side thrusts due to engine operation and ship rolling, thus minimising shear and bending stresses in the holding down studs. Side supports generally consist of buttressed bearing plates welded to the foundation plates, with taper chocks located between the bedplate and the bearing plate **(Figure 60)**.

Flexible or Resilient Mountings

The various kinds of flexible or resilient mounting all serve to keep the engine in the desired position and to prevent transmission of vibration to the hull of the ship. In passenger ships it is essential to avoid vibration and structure bourne noise in the accommodation spaces, and but the use of medium speed engines allows passenger spaces to be placed low down in the ship. It is possible to mount engines on a raft with integral vibration damping, but direct mounting of engines in the ship is simpler and less costly. Flexible/ resilient mountings are rubber based and may be of the inclined or vertical type. The rubber pads absorb noise and vibration energy. An effective resilient mounting system will provide an isolation factor of at least 50 to 80 per cent. Although rubber has excellent vibration damping properties, it is prone to damage by mineral oil, so the rubber mounts have to be protected against dripping and splashing by means of covers. Brackets for the rubber mounts are fitted on the foundation plate using steel or resin chocks. Buffers, similar to the flexible mountings, are fitted at the sides and ends of the engine. The flexible mountings must be carefully designed to ensure the attenuation of structure borne noise. This is closely linked with engine operating speed. For engines which are designed to operate over a speed range, e.g. CP propeller systems, it is essential that the system is designed to avoid problem speed areas. Some other speed ranges may be unusable due to torsional vibration **(Figure 61)**.

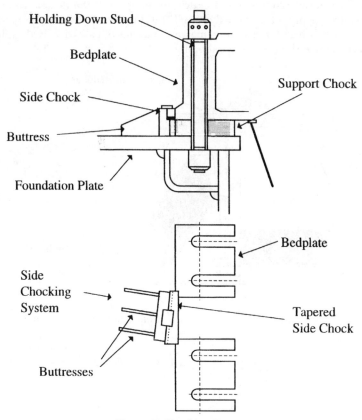

Figure 60. Chocking System

Flexible Connections and Pipework

When an engine is installed on flexible mountings, all connections to the engine must be flexible. All pipework, particularly exhaust trunking from the turbochargers to the uptakes, must have arrangements to absorb the engine displacements allowed by the flexible mountings. In addition, exhaust trunking and pipework must allow for thermal expansion. No gratings or ladders should be fixed to the actual engine.

Power Transmission from the Engine

Power transmission from the engine, except for electrical machines mounted on the same raft, should be accomplished by means of a flexible coupling or a combined flexible coupling and clutch. In many cases the flexible coupling and clutch are provided at the flywheel. The clutch is a critical component, as it must be capable of transmitting maximum torque but also deal with sudden load changes without excessive slipping.

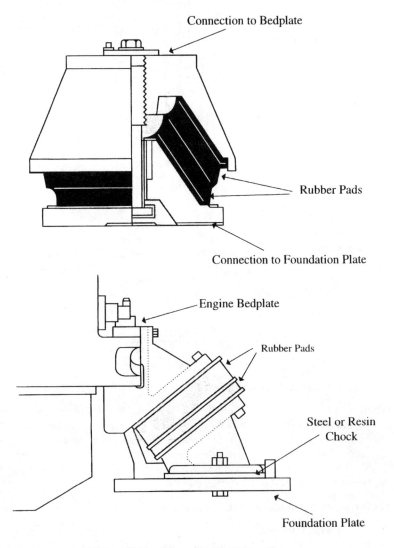

Connection to Bedplate

Rubber Pads

Connection to Foundation Plate

Engine Bedplate

Rubber Pads

Steel or Resin Chock

Foundation Plate

Figure 61. Flexible or Resilient Mountings

Torsional Vibration and Dampers

Torsional vibration can be a problem with some engine installations. It causes high shaft stresses at critical speeds, and a torsional vibration damper can reduce, shift or even eliminate a barred speed range. A torsional vibration damper will be fitted at the free end of the engine and may be of the viscous damping type for low energy vibrations, or the spring loaded type for high energy vibrations. Whether or not an engine requires a torsional vibration damper depends on many factors, including stiffness of the crankshaft, number of cylinders and operating speed.

Overhead Crane Systems

Engine maintenance requirements dictate that an overhead crane system must be provided to allow removal of the cylinder heads, pistons and liners. The minimum headroom requirement depends on the maximum length of the parts to be removed. The longest is usually the piston and its attached connecting rod. Special lifting tools are required for Vee engines to ensure all items may be lifted without damage.

Engine Room Services

Engine room services must meet the needs of the engines and other equipment. Cooling water, lubricating oil, fuel supply and starting air must meet the demands of the engine and the rules of the classification societies. Such systems are covered in more detail in other volumes in the MEP series.

Air Supply

Air supply to the engine must be sufficient to develop power without combustion problems. In normal circumstances most engines are supplied with at least 100 per cent excess air, and the engine room ventilation system should be capable of dealing with this. Engines always draw air directly from the engine room. An engine room ventilation system is generally sized so that it will supply twice the amount of air consumed by the engines. A number of air ducts should be placed close to the turbocharger inlets.

Exhaust Systems

Exhaust systems must allow free flow of exhaust gas from the engine, and pipes should be of sufficient diameter for this to occur. It is possible to calculate the density of exhaust gas leaving the turbocharger, provided the approximate composition and temperature are known. The air mass may be determined from fuel supply and air/fuel ratio requirements, and the volume flow may be calculated from this. Exhaust pipe sizes may then be determined using this information. Flow through the silencer and any exhaust gas boiler in the uptake must be as free as possible. The sizes of these components should be such that the exhaust is effectively silenced, with as little back pressure on the engine as possible.

Tools and Spares

Any machinery system requires tools for overhaul and spares for maintenance. All tools should be located as close to the engine as possible, and the supply of spares should be such that normal maintenance can readily be carried out. A comprehensive maintenance log should be kept, which not only allows engineers to examine the history of an engine for earlier problems, but also allows a check to be kept on excessive use of spares.

Summary of Engine Choice and Installation

Engine Choice:	Limited range available to suit speed and power requirements; choice is a compromise in many cases.
SFC:	Fuel costs are important and most builders aim for minimum SFC at about 85 per cent mcr.
Flexibility of system:	Use of multi-engine installations allows engines to be run close to mcr for minimum SFC. 'Father and son' systems with engines of different powers.
Load Diagrams:	Show where engine is to be operated for greatest efficiency and optimum loading. Links engine to propeller curve.
Flexible Mountings:	Minimise transmission of vibration to hull.
Chocking:	Needed to ensure the engine is aligned with other parts of the system.
Installation:	Allow for flexible connections of pipes, exhaust trunking and inspection gratings/ladders.

4   Operation

Running-In

Any new engine should undergo a running-in period to ensure all parts and services are functioning correctly. Rubbing surfaces at bearings, gears, cams and in the cylinders need particular attention. An abundant lubricant supply is required to ensure small metal particles are carried away from the mating surfaces. Cylinder liners and piston rings are perhaps the most critical items, as cylinder power development depends on the rings sealing effectively with the liner surface. New components will have machining marks, which prevent a good seal until the rings bed with the liner. Shipboard engineers are unlikely to be faced with a completely new engine, as a period of operating on the engine builder's test plant will have provided the initial running-in. However, it might be necessary to run a new engine on reduced load for a period of time. Running-in may also be required after an overhaul, and the builder's instructions must be followed meticulously to ensure the engine can subsequently be relied upon to develop the intended power. Although running-in is particularly needed after bearings, piston rings and cylinder liners are replaced, the procedures adopted following any overhaul should ensure the engine will perform as expected when full power is applied. Oil and coolant pressures must be monitored, and oil filters must be cleaned, as foreign particles are likely to find their way into the sump during any overhaul. Circulation of the oil for a period prior to starting the engine will help clean the system. A period on low load is needed to allow the piston rings to bed against the liner and so produce an effective seal which can subsequently take maximum cylinder pressure. Temperatures and pressure must be monitored for any abnormal values as the load is gradually increased over a period of time. Engine builders recommend periods of time at particular loads and these must be observed. A period of up to about 50 hours on low and intermediate loads, including test bed running, is typical before the engine can be expected to take full load.

Checks on New, Overhauled or Repaired Engines

Any new, overhauled or repaired engine should be given a thorough examination before it is put into service. Care should be taken to ensure that linkages from the control station to governor and fuel pumps are complete and free to move. Fuel pump settings should be checked so that cylinder loadings will reflect the control setting. It is particularly important that the no-fuel setting on the control gives zero fuel from individual fuel pumps. All coolant and lubricant flow pipes should be free from leakage, and fuel lines should be primed so that fuel is available at the injectors. Where residual fuel is used it is necessary to ensure that the heater is functioning correctly and that the temperature/viscosity control is operational. The camshaft system must be checked to make certain that all cylinder valves will function correctly when the engine operates. The engine may be turned using the turning gear to allow these checks to be carried out, but it is important that the pre-lubrication system is operated beforehand. Where an electric motor is used for turning the engine, a note should be made of the electric motor ammeter reading prior to overhaul so that this can be compared with the reading after overhaul. If the reading increases it will indicate some tightness at a bearing or other part of the system, and the cause should be investigated.

Checks Prior to Starting

The air receiver(s) should be filled to the correct pressure prior to starting. After opening the main valve to the air start control station, checks should be made for leakage. Although remote starting from the bridge is usual with engines used for propulsion, the initial start after an overhaul or with a new engine should be from the local control station. The engine should be run on test for a period prior to being put on load. If a slow turning facility is provided with the air start system, this will function automatically prior to starting. However, it is still advisable to turn the engine for at least two revolutions with the turning gear to ensure it is free to turn. Most control systems allow an automatic change to fuel when sufficient rotational speed on air has been achieved. With all cylinders firing on fuel, control can be passed to the governor, which will allow for no-load rotation at the pre-set speed. Load should gradually be applied to the engine, and only when the operating engineer is satisfied that the engine is functioning normally without any signs which might indicate an operational problem. It was formerly practice to run the engine for a period following bearing overhaul and then stop to allow manual investigation for signs of overheating. In all but the smallest engines this is no longer necessary, as instrumentation allows monitoring of all bearing temperatures. Such instrumentation should always be checked prior to starting the engine.

Tests on Running Engines

Many items on an engine can only be tested while the engine is running. This is particularly the case for cylinder combustion. Fuel pumps will have been tested and set ashore, and the lifting pressure of fuel injectors will also have been set away from the engine. However, cylinder performance can only be assessed with the engine operating. Electronic systems are available which allow cylinder peak pressure, fuel injection timing and even cylinder power to be assessed. Such systems are of great benefit, as they enable the engineer to balance cylinder powers quickly and accurately. Because of the operating speed of medium speed engines, use of a conventional indicator is not practical; inertia forces in the drum prevent accurate indicator cards being taken. Cylinder powers can be assessed relative to each other by considering peak cylinder pressures, exhaust temperatures and test-bed data for similar powers, yet the system is still not precise. In some cases cylinder compression pressures can also be taken, which allows the condition of cylinder valves and piston rings to be assessed. Exhaust temperatures from cylinders will never be identical even though cylinders might be developing the same power, so no attempt should be made to equalise exhaust temperatures. The timing of fuel injection has a great influence on engine dynamic loadings and many factors have to be considered when dealing with cylinder fuel adjustment. Incorrect adjustment can result in damage to bearings, piston rings and in the combustion space due to flame impingement. Electronic systems calculate cylinder power, and allow readings of cylinder parameters such as injection timing to be obtained instantly, which means a true assessment of the engine can be made very quickly. Individual cylinder powers can be adjusted but this means that fuel injection timing must be considered as well as the quantity of fuel injected. If cylinder conditions appear abnormal there may be other reasons apart from fuel; this can relate to leaking valves or piston rings. Electronic systems can also provide advice to the engineer on engine adjustments (see Chapter 5).

Cylinder Power Balance

Perfect power balance is impossible to achieve, as engine parts wear at different rates. Even with completely new engines, all parts of the system will not be identical. However, to minimise operating problems, it is important that the powers developed by individual cylinders are as close as possible. Should one cylinder develop less power, the governor will automatically increase loadings on other cylinders to maintain the desired total output. Some cylinders can thus become overloaded. Any fall-off in performance of one cylinder will increase the load differential with other cylinders by an amount greater than the overall power change. Higher loading on other cylinders can cause deterioration due to burning at valves and damage to piston rings. This, in turn, results in reduced load development and consequent increase in load on other cylinders. The power differentials increase until a few cylinders are overloaded, at which point major problems are likely to occur, particularly if the engine is operating close to its mcr. It is important that frequent checks are made on an engine in order to assess performance and early action must be taken if any change in power balance is noted. With engines fitted with full monitoring and diagnostic systems, this can readily be done daily. For other engines, a widening in the spread of exhaust temperatures is an early indication of poor power balance.

Fuel Quantity Adjustment

Fuel quantity can be adjusted using the screwed linkage which connects the fuel pump rack with the regulating shaft lever. This adjustment should only be by a small amount at a time, and the effect on the engine should be noted at each adjustment. Fuel pump racks are usually marked with graduations or indices. With new pumps these should all be the same, but as adjustments take place for wear they will differ. The amount of any adjustment of the screwed linkage should be noted in relation to the fuel pump index reading. The screwed linkage should be locked by means of the lock nuts to prevent accidental change of the setting caused by vibration. Care must be taken to ensure that any adjustment does not interfere with the ability of the governor or control linkage to shut off the fuel. Moving the regulating shaft to the fuel off position must always result in the pumps ceasing to deliver fuel. Fuel pumps are always set so that there is no fuel delivery during the first few millimetres of rack movement, which allows adjustment of the regulating shaft stop position. The need for fuel pump quantity adjustment results from wear at the sharp edges on the plunger helix and on the spill port (see Chapter 2, Figure 40). If these sharp edges become rounded at a particular plunger rotational position, the spill port will be covered later on the plunger up stroke. This causes delayed injection, which must be countered by raising the plunger relative to the spill port by some means (see Chapter 2, Injection Timing). At the same rotational position of the plunger, the lower face of the helix will uncover the spill port earlier on its upward stroke, resulting in less fuel being injected. The plunger is rotated slightly to correct this, at the same fuel regulating setting, by adjustment of the screwed linkage to give the original effective stroke of the plunger and hence the same quantity of fuel delivery as previously. If the plunger has a flat top, this rotational adjustment does not have any influence on the timing of the beginning of fuel injection.

Engine Monitoring

The engine must be monitored during normal service so that changes in performance may be detected before they cause problems. Traditional arrangements involved visual checks and notes in a log book each four hour watch period, along with alarms for the likes of lubricating oil and cooling water pressures and temperatures. Information, of course, only becomes useful if it is put to use. Electronic monitoring systems not only provide regular monitoring of many engine parameters but they also analyse the data, allowing trends in performance to be highlighted. Performance monitoring is covered fully in chapter 5, but it is important to realise that data acquisition and analysis is only as good as the equipment used to obtain and interrogate that data. Checks must be made on transducer performance, the data transmission systems and on the equipment being used to perform the analysis. The levels at which alarms sound must be checked and adjusted so that the duty engineer is not disturbed unnecessarily. Electronic equipment does fail, but many monitoring systems are self checking and so will detect and report failed items. Transducers, cables and other parts of the monitoring equipment are just as much part of a diesel engine installation as the fuel pumps or injectors and, deserve similar attention if the plant is to perform to expectation.

Exhaust Emissions

Exhaust emissions have latterly come to present problems for the operator of marine diesel engines, particularly with respect to oxides of nitrogen (NO_x). Oxides of sulphur (SO_x) are a problem but this can only be overcome in the marine world by burning low or zero sulphur fuels and so is not related to engine operation. NO_x forms in the combustion zone when oxygen and nitrogen in the atmosphere is heated to high temperature during combustion and then cooled rapidly; an important factor governing the formation of NO_x is the length of time spent at high temperature. It should be noted that NO_x formation is independent of the fuel burned. NO_x emissions can be controlled through primary or secondary methods, although the secondary method, involving as it does a catalytic unit in the funnel uptake, lies well outside the scope of the present work. Primary methods related to the actual engine may, however, be considered. NO_x forms when nitrogen and oxygen are heated to high temperature during fuel combustion, and if the maximum cylinder temperature can be reduced less NO_x will form.

Exhaust Gas Recirculation

Exhaust Gas Recirculation (EGR) is a means of reducing NO_x formation in which some of the exhaust gas is drawn back into the engine, which reduces the percentage of oxygen in the 'air' charge drawn into the cylinders. This means that there is less oxygen available for combustion and the formation of NO_x in the first place, and since the fuel has first call on the oxygen, it is employed for combustion, leaving even less available for NO_x formation. There is a full charge of 'air' in the cylinder, which is heated, but combustion is slower because of the reduced oxygen content. As a result, the maximum cylinder temperature is lower and less NO_x forms. The amount of exhaust gas recirculated must be kept under control, or cylinder combustion will suffer **(Figure 62)**.

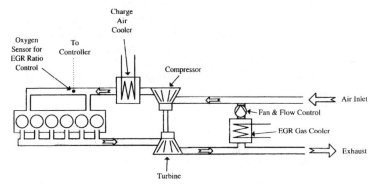

Figure 62. Exhaust Gas Recirculation (EGR) System

Fumigation

Maximum cylinder temperature can be reduced by injecting water into the cylinder, a process known as fumigation. Some of the energy released during combustion must be employed in evaporating the water and even dissociating the steam. With a lower maximum temperature, less NOx is generated, but energy from the expanding steam and possible subsequent combining of the oxygen and hydrogen from dissociation allow some of the energy imparted to the water to be reclaimed. The quantity of water injected must be carefully regulated or performance can suffer. The use of emulsified fuel has a similar effect to water injection **(Figure 63)**.

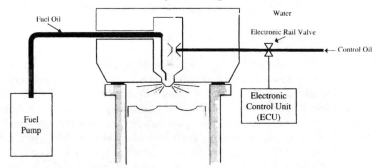

Figure 63. Water Injection System

Control systems for EGR and water injection must be monitored to ensure they only allow the correct quantity of exhaust gas or water into the cylinder. If control is not exact, the engine may be damaged and the NO_x emission level will not be reduced.

Summary of Operation

Running in:
Period of low power operation required with new or overhauled engine to ensure that the piston rings form a seal with the liner and that bearings bed-in effectively.

Clean crankcase:
Circulation of lubricating oil following an overhaul to ensure that foreign matter is removed.

Test engine before starting:
Slow turning on reduced pressure to check for hydraulic lock.Low load running for short period to test new bearing surfaces.

Cylinder power balance:
Electronic systems allow actual power to be assessed. Fuel injection timing and quantity affect on power development.

Fuel pump adjustment:
Need to adjust timing and quantity. Timing adjustment by altering position of plunger relative to the spill port, e.g. shims between plunger foot and tappet. Adjust quantity by rotating plunger using screwed link; link must be locked to avoid change in setting due to vibration.

Monitoring engine parameters:
Accurate and frequent checks on operating parameters to avoid damage due to maloperation. Electronic system gives frequent scanning and allows analysis of data. Electronic system should be self checking.

Emission control:
NO_x emission levels may be reduced by exhaust gas recirculation, water injection or the use of emulsified fuel.

5 Operational Support Systems and Performance Monitoring

Engine Management Systems

An engine management system not only allows for monitoring and remote control, but also provides the operator with computer based tools for improving economy and assessing maintenance requirements. A network of sensors mounted in various parts of the engine transmits data about operating conditions to the computer at the heart of the system. As with any management system the quality of the decisions made depends on the information provided, so it is essential that sensors are correctly placed and of high quality. The operator has little choice in placing the sensors but he can ensure that they are not damaged during overhaul and that the signal transmission systems do not suffer from external influences such as vibration, heat and electromagnetic interference.

Each engine builder has their own management system, with computer software written to suit the particular engines in a range, however, the underlying principles tend to be broadly similar. Systems can become complex as 'add-on' sub-systems are added, such as arrangements to provide guidance on preventive maintenance and spares ordering. The basic system allows engine parameters to be monitored, and permits the logging of data, alarm conditions and remote starting and stopping.

Engine Sensors

Engine sensors monitor cylinder and other engine conditions. The sensors feed information to the computer, which monitors and acts on this data. Any action taken depends on how the computer in question has been programmed. In many cases all engine sensors connect with a central terminal box mounted on the engine, which feeds the engine management computer via a single armoured and screened cable. The requirements of a sensor depend on the task it is to perform, and all sensors have optimum operating ranges. It is therefore essential that the correct device is fitted if the signal generated is to accurately reflect the parameter being monitored. A similar situation exists with respect to the signal transmission system, so signal transmission cables should not be altered without consulting the system designer.

Engine Alarms

Classification societies require certain engine conditions to be monitored and alarm settings to be provided. However, there is no complete agreement between classification societies as to which parameters should be monitored for alarm. The list given in Table 1 indicates the general situation for sample engine systems. It is usual for an alarm to be activated as soon as a pressure or temperature falls to a preset value. Action can then be taken by the engine operator. Should the situation not improve after a set interval of time, an engine slowdown operation will be activated. If the situation does not improve after a further interval, an engine shutdown routine is activated. Certain parameters such as cooling water temperature and pressure will generally have alarm, slowdown and shutdown routines with up to a 60 second delay before the shutdown procedure begins. Safety devices such as the crankcase oil mist detector will not allow such long intervals and many can be set to activate the engine shutdown procedure system after an interval as short as 10 seconds. Other systems monitored for alarms will include fuel oil, exhaust gas, charge air, starting air, control air and bearing temperatures **(Table 1)** .

Medium	Unit	Location	Function	Setting	Time delay
High Temperature Cooling Water	Pressure	Engine Inlet	Alarm	3.5 bar	0 sec
			Slow Down	3.0 bar	20 sec
			Shut Down	3.0 bar	60 sec
	Temperature	Engine Outlet	Alarm	95^{0}C	0 sec
			Slow Down	97^{0}C	20 sec
			Shut Down	97^{0}C	60 sec
Low Temperature Cooling Water	Pressure	Pump Outlet	Alarm	2.0 bar	0 sec
	Temperature	CAC Inlet	Alarm	25^{0}C	60 sec
		CAC Outlet	Alarm	55^{0}C	60 sec
Fuel Nozzle Cooling	Pressure	Engine Inlet	Alarm	2.0 bar	0 sec
	Temperature	Engine Outlet	Alarm	70^{0}C	0 sec
Lubricating Oil	Pressure	Engine Inlet	Alarm	4.0 bar	0 sec
			Slow Down	3.0 bar	20 sec
			Shut Down	3.0 bar	60 sec
	Temp	Engine Inlet	Alarm	60^{0}C	0 sec
			Slow Down	65^{0}C	20 sec
			Shut Down	65^{0}C	60 sec
	Oil Mist Detector	Crankcase	Alarm		0 sec
			Slow Down		2 sec
			Shut Down		10 sec

Table 1. Monitoring Systems and Associated Operational Data

Data Acquisition, Display and Storage

The engine management system must analyse the data coming in from its sensors, which are scanned as often as twice per second. Any action taken with the raw data depends on the individual system, but certain information will be displayed on Visual Display Units (VDUs) on the bridge and at the engine room control station. There will also be displays available at other locations including the cabins of duty engineers. Not all information gathered will be displayed, to avoid overloading the duty or operating engineer with information. Displays may also indicate alarm conditions. Most information gathered will be stored to allow trends to be determined. Adequate computer storage is, therefore, required together with a data backup storage system.

Engine Control Station Displays

Some engine builders, such as Wärtsilä, provide engine displays at the engine control station itself as well as at the remote control station. This allows the duty engineer to see locally the effect of any action taken. The Wärtsilä Engine Control System (WECS) is standard on the Wärtsilä Vasa 32 engine, and consists of a main control cabinet mounted on the engine. This cabinet houses the main control unit, a local display unit, control buttons and back-up instruments. Distributed control units are located at certain parts of the engine to actuate devices at these location. Sensor multiplexing units, also located around the engine, gather data from various sensors and send this information to the main control unit. This integrated form of automation allows the engine to be a self contained unit while allowing all data from the sensors to be directed back to a central engine management system from the single WECS cabinet.

Data Analysis

The provision of engine control, an alarm and data logging is just part of an engine management system. The computer can analyse data gathered from the engine and then provide valuable assistance in the operation and maintenance of the engine. Trend analysis enables the operator to see how the engine is behaving over a period of time. The computer can, with suitable software, offer advice as to the best way to maintain the engine in optimum operating condition. Deterioration in fuel injectors, fuel pumps or cylinder piston rings may not be obvious from raw data, but by looking at other engine parameters one can detect a fall-off in performance of a single engine feature long before it triggers an alarm. The software, if written for the purpose, can give an indication as to when a particular item should be replaced after a period of further operation. The air and water surfaces of a charge air cooler may occasionally need to be cleaned of deposits. The pressure drop across the air side of the cooler can indicate the need for cleaning of the air side. By monitoring that pressure drop for each second of operation at different loads, the computer can predict when cleaning should be carried out, bearing in mind the operational requirements of the engine. Trend analysis can be performed on all engine systems, but software needs to be written to enable current data to be considered alongside other engine conditions and historical data. Accurate parameter monitoring and recording is an important part of trend analysis.

Dedicated Diagnostic Systems

Trend analysis can be considered as part of the engine diagnostic system, however, there are other, more dedicated diagnostic systems which can perform their function on-line. These aim to detect potential engine failures which could result in economic, safety or environmental problems. Diagnostic systems indicate the health of the engine and show where and how faults, which could influence performance or even result in failure of a system, might be developing. To diagnose a problem the computer must first receive information regarding the engine operation from the system of sensors fitted to the engine. Vibration sensors at turbocharger bearings will indicate possible problems related to bearings or surging of the blower, while piston ring wear sensors located in the cylinder (e.g. the Sulzer SIPWA system) detect problems related to piston ring damage or excessive wear. The SIPWA system monitors the rings as they pass sensors located in the liner, so any damaged rings can readily be detected. Ring wear can also be sensed and compared with previous readings, taken over many hours of service, enabling the system to assess the rate at which wear is taking place. It can then offer recommendations based on the information stored in the computer database. On-line computer based diagnosis requires current and historic engine information to be analysed before the computer can offer suggestions as to the action required to improve performance or avoid failure. The knowledge-based diagnostic system employs information gathered from many thousands of hours of operation with the particular type of equipment under consideration. It does not replace the engineer, but it provides another tool to enable the correct decisions to be made.

Satellite Links

Although on board systems can function in isolation, diagnostic systems can be linked to shore-based computers via satellite. Information can be updated from many similar engines operating throughout the world but software operating on board ship can also be upgraded the moment any improvements are made.

Computer Systems and Maintenance

Computer systems can also be used to organise maintenance requirements. Planned maintenance may be organised by the computer but condition-based maintenance offers the best opportunity to ensure that the engine performs to expectation, by offering advice as to the most appropriate maintenance schedule. Computer software can also manage the use of spares. A check can be kept as to the spares used and those remaining on board and spare gear orders can be generated and placed automatically via the computer.

Performance Monitoring

No matter how good the computer based monitoring and diagnostic system, engineers are still required to implement maintenance and to carry out most engine adjustments to ensure optimum performance. Performance monitoring is not simply a matter of calculating cylinder power because performance is not just power developed. Performance relates to how efficiently and effectively the power is generated. It involves fuel consumption, lubricating oil consumption and the use of spares as well as the engine down-time needed to achieve such performance. Control of emissions forms an essential part of engine operation as it is necessary to comply with regulations regarding exhaust emission levels. Certain emissions can also indicate poor cylinder combustion performance, therefore, correct positioning of emission monitoring sensors is essential to control.[1] Sensors at the cylinder, fuel injection system and on the output shaft allow cylinder and engine output power to be determined. There is no longer any need to take peak pressures or otherwise manually monitor the cylinder. Once the cylinder power being developed by all cylinders has been determined, the computer system can relate this to the exhaust temperatures and fuel injection timing, via sensors on the fuel pumps and the output shaft, to assess how effectively the fuel is being burned. Using a knowledge-based system, suggestions can be offered as to how performance might be improved. Fuel consumption is measured at engine inlet but the quantity used at each cylinder can be assessed by considering the timing and fuel pump settings. Turbocharger performance also needs to be assessed as does the effectiveness of the cooling system as all of these factors influence the overall engine performance. Knowledge-based monitoring and diagnostic systems are important to modern engines which have to operate for long periods of time without stopping for an overhaul. The system is, however, only as good as the individual parts, so effective performance of sensors is critical. Defective sensors and signal transmission systems will produce false data, therefore the operator should ensure that they are protected from damage.

Hardware/Software Packages

Engine builders provide integrated hardware/software packages for engine systems. Such packages can include data acquisition and display, alarms, trend analysis, condition monitoring, performance monitoring, on-line diagnostics, expert systems for advice, maintenance planning, repair action and spare gear organisation. The operator must be trained to make full use of the system **(Figure 64)**.

---

1. For further information on Emissions and exhaust combustion see Marine Engineering Practice Series, Volume 3, Part 20, *Exhaust Emissions from Combustion Machinery* by A A Wright - published July 1999.

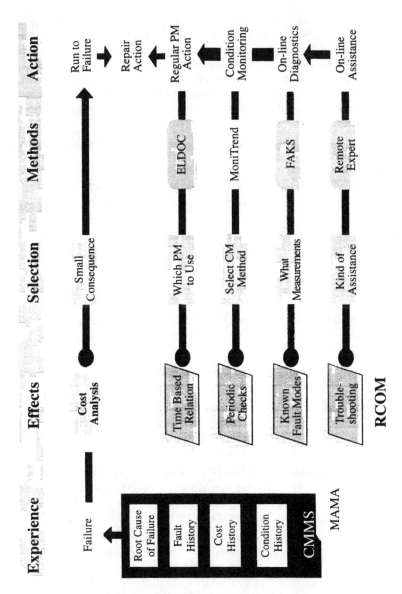

Figure 64. Diagrammatic Arrangement of the
Wärtsilä Integrated Engine System Package

Emergency Local Control Systems

Control systems allow remote starting and stopping of the engine but there must always be a local system for emergency operation. It is usual to arrange for the engine to have a slow turning system before full starting air pressure is applied, and for load to be applied slowly. Power management systems will arrange for the standby engine to start when the load dictates. All systems will operate as for a manual start, with load transfer taking place slowly. A period of pre-lubrication is essential prior to starting the engine to prevent bearing damage.

Summary of Operational Support Systems & Performance Monitoring

Engine Management System (EMS):	Computer based system for organisation of engine control, operation and maintenance.
Engine Sensors:	Must be suited for purpose and location. Signal transmission system must be protected against interference or damage.
Alarm Settings:	Must comply with classification society requirements regarding type and location. Must enable slow down or shut down after predetermined time.
Local Engine Control:	Control and monitoring system available at engine to provide backup.
Trend Analysis:	Information from engine used to determine trends in performance and produce predictions regarding optimum maintenance schedule.
Diagnostic System:	On-line diagnosis of engine condition from engine operating information allows for report on engine health, and indicates future probable failure or damage.
Expert or Knowledge Based Systems:	On board computer based system which allow wide operating experience, gathered from other engines of the type, to be used to diagnose faults and predict problems.
Maintenance:	Schedules can be predicted and spare gear organised by linking computer systems with information from the engine.

Integrated Engine Management Systems: Engine builders provide integrated systems to allow control and maintenance of the engine, prediction of failure and optimisation of performance. Software can be updated by satellite links and data can be exchanged with the engine builder and owner.

6   Maintenance

Maintenance Requirements

Maintenance requirements depend on engine operating conditions. Although engine builders indicate running hours for overhaul of particular components, they are for guidance purposes only. The quality of the fuel being burnt has a marked effect on the operating life of cylinder components. The use of diesel oil will markedly increase the interval between overhaul, however, economics dictate the use of residual fuels in most cases, so a reduction in operating intervals between maintenance has to be accepted. Overall economics based on the operating life of the engine should take into account the total cost of maintenance, spares, labour and downtime, as well as the cost of fuel and lube oil.

Planned Maintenance

Planned maintenance essentially dictates overhaul after a set period of running. The number of running hours will be suggested by the engine builder based on experience. As already stated, the interval can be reduced or increased in service by many factors, including the fuel being burnt and the actual load on the engine. Low load operation does not necessarily imply a longer interval between overhaul as low loads can mean less efficient cylinder combustion, which can cause deposits to build up on injector nozzles, cylinder valves and turbocharger blades. It may, in some cases, affect the guarantee provided by the builder. The engine operator should be prepared to adjust the running hours between overhaul in the light of his own service experience. Part of any planned maintenance system is routine inspection, which consists of checks rather than actually removing the engine parts for cleaning or replacement. Such inspection may be carried out manually at the engine or by means of sensors, but normal practice is to use a combination of the two. As with all equipment, frequent checking can provide valuable information as to the actual running thereby reducing the need for unplanned maintenance. A typical planned inspection and maintenance routine would be similar to that shown in Table 2. This Table indicates the inspection and maintenance routine up to 2000 running hours. Some of the procedures are only undertaken with a new engine, and subsequent intervals for the same operation are extended. Many items on an engine are subject to less frequent maintenance and there would be routines for say 4000 hour intervals, 8000 hour intervals, 16 000 hour intervals, etc. Obviously, those items requiring attention at, say, 500 hour intervals would receive that attention every 500 running hours and not just after the initial 500 hours of operation. **(Table 2)**

System	Action	
Every second day whether engine in operation or not		
Automatic Prelubrication	Check operation	
Crankshaft	Turn to new position	
Each week		
Start System	Test start (if stand by engine)	
50 Operating hour interval		
Air Coolers	Check drains	*Clear any blockage*
Cooling Water System	Check coolant level	*Top up as necessary*
Connecting Rod	Check tightness of bolts	*Hydraulic pump to stated pressure but do not loosen*
Fuel & Lube Oil Filters	Check pressure drop	*Clean or replace if necessary*
Gauges & Indicators	Take readings under load	*Check and record readings; compare with previous values*
Governor	Check oil level & linkages	*Top up as needed*
Fuel Injection System	Check fuel pumps	*Check pump and injector leak quantity*
Lube Oil Sump	Check oil level	*Top up as necessary*
Main Bearings	Check tightness of cap screws	*Hydraulic pump to stated pressure but do not loosen*
Turbocharger	Water wash compressor Check oil level	*Test after cleaning* *Top up and look for leaks*
Valve Mechanism	Check valve clearance	*For new and overhauled engines*
250 Operating hour interval		
Turbocharger	Water wash turbine	*Check after cleaning and repeat if necessary*
Control Mechanism	Check operation	*Check for free movement , clean and lubricate*
500 Operating hour interval		
Cooling Water	Check water quality	*Test or additive level*
Lubricating Oil	Take Sample	*For new engine or oil change*
Turbocharger	Change lube oil	*Drain thoroughly*
1000 Operating hour intervals		
Automation	Check functioning	*Check alarm & automatic stop devices*
Fuel & Lube Oil Filters	Replace	
Valves	Check valve condition	*Check freedom of movement and clearance*
2000 Operating hour intervals		
Air Coolers	Check water side	*Clean. New engine then at 4000 hour intervals*
Injectors	Inspect and test	*Check lifting pressure. Dismantle and clean. Replace nozzles as necessary*
Lubricating Oil	Change oil charge	*New engine then 8000 hours*

Table 2. Inspection and Maintenance Routine to 2000 Hours

Re-Use of Components

Correctly maintained and overhauled components can be reused in the engine. Engine builders will give indications as to the expected service life of components, assuming their recommendations regarding maintenance have been followed and that approved spares have been used. The quality of spare gear – in terms of materials and manufacture – has a critical influence on the service life of a component. Only approved spares should be used. Table 3 shows typical service life expectations for major engine components **(Table 3)**.

Component	Maintenance Interval (1000 hours)	Service Life (1000 hours)
Piston Crown	30-40	60-80
First Piston Ring		12-15
Cylinder Liner	12-15	60-80
Inlet Valve Cone	12-15	30-40
Exhaust Valve Cone	6-10	30
Exhaust Valve Cage	6-10	30-40
Fuel Pump Element		25-35
Fuel Injection Nozzle	3	6-10
Main/Conn Rod Bearing		30-40
Turbocharger Bearing		20-30

Table 3. Typical Service Life Expectations for Major Engine Components

Other Maintenance Issues

While planned maintenance is extremely useful, as it allows maintenance schedules to be organised to fit in with the ship's operating schedule, it does have its problems. Components do not wear or suffer damage at the same rate and a defective component can damage other components. For example, a defective injector nozzle can damage exhaust valves and piston rings causing deterioration long before the running hour interval for overhaul is reached. The operating engineer must be aware of such issues and be willing to adjust maintenance accordingly. The use of computer based diagnostic systems can both provide evidence of component deterioration and allow maintenance decisions to be made on the basis of need. Preventive maintenance is always better than breakdown maintenance! Classification societies require engine components to be surveyed every four years, or five if a rolling maintenance programme is in operation. It is usual to arrange for routine maintenance to fit in with the survey programme, wherever possible, so effective organisation of running hours is required.

Standard Maintenance Routines and Checks

In practice, the choice of maintenance system will depend on a number of factors, and the operator will have to take into account emergencies which can disrupt any maintenance schedule. It is essential for defective components to be replaced or repaired as soon as possible, to prevent problems elsewhere in the engine which increase the maintenance requirement. Whatever the choice of system, there are features common to all, which should be observed.

Lifting Gear

All lifting gear used for maintenance should have the appropriate certification, and a routine should be adopted which will ensure all items of lifting equipment are tested at the correct time and replaced as necessary.

Hydraulic Tools

All large nuts and screws on an engine are tightened and loosened by hydraulics, which should be checked as part of any routine maintenance. Particular attention should be paid to the O-ring seals employed with such hydraulic tools. Damaged seals can fail causing a high pressure jet of oil to be released, which may injure personnel. Where a number of nuts hold a component the hydraulic tensioning jacks are generally arranged as a group, and should always be treated as a matching set. The set of jacks is pressurised from the same pump, so all screws are subjected to the same tension and the item being fitted is evenly loaded **(Figure 65)**.

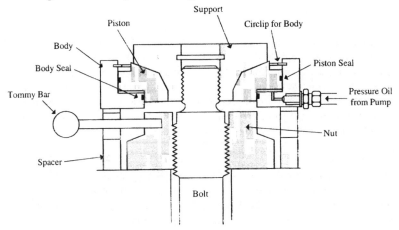

Figure 65. Hydraulic Jack for Tightening Nuts

Removing Nuts

When removing nuts, the hydraulic jack units should be screwed onto the threaded section at the top of the stud or bolt. Care must be taken to ensure the correct spacer is located below the hydraulic unit. The jack should be screwed down against the spacer then turned back about a quarter turn to provide clearance. The jack, or set of jacks, is then subjected to hydraulic pressure from a pump. This increases the tension in the stud or bolt and allows the nut to be unscrewed using the Tommy bar. When the nut has been unscrewed about one turn, the hydraulic unit(s) can be removed and nuts removed normally. All safety precautions must be observed, such as ensuring that the component being removed is adequately supported.

Tightening Nuts

When tightening nuts, the hydraulic units are fitted in the same way as for removal of nuts. The jack is loaded to a predetermined pressure to extend the stud or bolt by the desired amount to provide the correct tension. The nut is then turned down the thread until it touches its landing face. Hydraulic pressure is released and the jack mechanism removed.

Spares

Accurate records of spare gear on board should be kept. The spares carried should always comply with the requirements of the appropriate classification society. Approved spares should always be ordered immediately to replace items used in maintenance.

Record Keeping

Running hour and maintenance records should be maintained for all items of plant, with notes to indicate any problems during operation or defects observed during maintenance. Such records not only show that maintenance has been carried out, but also highlight areas or components which might be unusually troublesome. This could indicate a faulty batch of spares or a defect in operation which was not directly apparent. Computer-based trend analysis and diagnostic systems are of great help in this aspect of engine maintenance, but sensors only detect operational information, so defects observed during maintenance should be manually recorded.

During Overhaul

During any overhaul, parts should be carefully inspected for signs of cracking and fretting at contact faces. If there are any defects the component should be replaced and the cause of the problem investigated. Defects do not necessarily mean the component must be scrapped, but replacing them means that the engine can be returned to service quickly, allowing detailed examination and repair of the component later, where appropriate.

Prior to Maintenance

Prior to any maintenance the appropriate manual should be consulted to ensure all personnel involved understand the procedure to be carried out. Checks should be made to ensure the correct spares are available, including all joints and sealing rings, and that the specialist tools are functioning correctly.

Investigation of Defects

The cause of any defects found during maintenance should be investigated and corrected before the engine is returned to service. Simply replacing damaged parts is not a solution, as if there is an operational fault which is not corrected, new parts will suffer the same damage.

6.1   THE CRANKCASE

Crankshaft Alignment

Crankshaft alignment should be checked by taking deflections at intervals of about 4000 hours. Deflections are not taken on some small engines with rigid crankshafts but, for the majority of engines, this method provides the best means of assessing crankshaft alignment. In large engines, hull distortion can influence deflection readings, and as far as possible they, should be taken under the same load and trim conditions as previous sets in order to allow accurate comparison. Holding down arrangements should be checked for tightness as loose chocks can also influence readings. Deflections should be taken while the engine is warm to avoid the influence of thermal expansion. In engines with rigid crankshafts, checks should be made to ensure all journals are sitting in their bearings. When the engine is operating, pressures on the pistons will ensure the crankshaft journals are forced onto their bearings. Since there is no piston loading while taking deflections, if the weight of the running gear is insufficient to allow this to happen, false deflection readings will be obtained.

Deflection Gauge Fitting and Calibration

The deflection gauge must be fitted at the marked position between the webs of each unit, and the procedure repeated until readings are obtained from all units. Dial type deflection gauges may be used but electronic gauges are also available. Whatever the type the gauge should be calibrated to ensure accuracy, and must be zeroed once fitted between the webs. The first position, with the gauge at zero, is close to the piston bottom dead centre with the connection rod clear of the gauge – the 0° position. The crankshaft is turned and readings are taken at 90° intervals until the piston is again close to bottom dead centre, with the connection rod on the opposite side of the gauge. At this position (360°), the reading should have returned to zero. The procedure is repeated for all units.

Deflection Readings

Deflection readings are recorded on forms provided by the engine builder and the results are checked with values given in the instruction manual. Vertical misalignment, due to bearing wear or bedplate distortion, is indicated by the difference between top and bottom deflection readings – the difference between the 180° reading and the average of the 0° and 360° readings. Actual values of permitted deflection readings depend on many factors including cylinder bore, the stiffness of the crankshaft, and the distance between bearing centres. Engine builders provide guidance figures for all engines and if readings obtained fall outside the maximum permitted value, action should be taken to rectify the crankshaft alignment. This means adjustment or replacement of bearings. As most engines employ thin shell bearings which have no facility for adjustment, replacement is normal practice.

Journal Bearings

Journal bearings (see Chapter 2, 'Crankshaft and Main Bearings') should be replaced as a set (upper and lower shells). The choice of procedure depends on whether the crankshaft is of the underslung type or not. With an underslung arrangement, the lower, load bearing, shell comes clear with the cap when the bearing cap is released. The weight of the crankshaft means that there is no loading on the upper shell, which can readily be removed by rotating it out of its housing. Bearing shells should be inspected on front and back surfaces and the journal pin should also be examined for signs of cracking, scuffing, corrosion and other damage. New shells can be fitted, after checking that they are the correct size and undamaged, and the bearing cap can be hydraulically tightened to give the correct 'nip'. With a traditional form of crankshaft support the upper cap may be removed and the top shell taken out, but it is the lower shell which is subject to the load and therefore to wear. Jacking the crankshaft slightly will release pressure on the lower shell, which can be rotated around the journal. A new lower shell is fitted while the crankshaft is still raised. Following re-assembly a new set of deflection readings should be taken to check the problem has been corrected. If these readings are still outside acceptable limits, problems could exist with the chocking or with wear in the bearing shell housings. A check should have been made for loose chocks prior to taking deflections. With an underslung crankshaft, a worn bearing shell housing can be detected by examining the bearing cap which has been removed, however, for a conventional bedplate the crankshaft must be raised.

Bearing Shell Replacement

During routine inspection of journal and bearings (at about 16 000 hour intervals) and at routine Classification Society surveys it is not always necessary to replace bearing shells unless they show signs of damage or excessive wear. However, replacement of bearings may be appropriate at routine inspections if there is a risk they will exceed their maximum wear limit before the next routine inspection is due. Much depends on the running hours since the last replacement and the condition of the bearing. Tri-metal type bearing shells can be used until the overlay has worn through but when the nickel barrier is exposed they must be replaced. Bi-metal bearings must be measured to establish the amount of wear; a ball anvil micrometer is used for this purpose and engine builders will provide details of wear limits for different sizes of bearing. The back of the bearing shell should also be inspected and the bearings replaced if there are signs of fretting, wear or corrosion. Both shells must be replaced with a matched pair and all protective material removed from the shells before they are fitted. Where bearings act as thrust bearings, the axial clearance between the sides of the shell and the rubbing face on the crankshaft should be measured. The bearing shells must be replaced if this exceeds the recommended value.

Torsional Vibration Dampers

Torsional vibration dampers differ from engine type to engine type, and only require attention at about 24 000 hour intervals. At this point they should be dismantled and all parts checked for wear or other damage. Oil samples from viscous type dampers should be taken at about 16 000 hour intervals and sent for analysis.

Large End Bearings

Large end bearings are treated in the same way as main bearings, and similar conditions apply regarding inspection and replacement. Clearances can be checked with feeler gauges, and for many engines it is possible to lift pistons without disturbing the large end bearing (see Chapter 2, 'Connection Rods'). Inspection of large end bearings should take place at intervals between 8000 hours and 12 000 hours. Crankpins should be inspected for signs of corrosion and other damage and checked for ovality using a micrometer. The bore of the large end bearing can be checked by assembling the lower portion of the connection rod away from the engine. Care should be taken to tension the large end bolts correctly. Vee type engines have multiple bearing arrangements for their large ends which usually means that a complete set of bearings is replaced if replacement is required.

Large End Bolts

Large end bolts and their nuts are subject to tensile stress when tightened and additional varying tensile stress during operation. The total stress level is high and varies with time, giving rise to the risk of fatigue. Over-tensioning of bolts should be avoided as this increases the stress level. If bolts are damaged during maintenance, stress raisers will result, thereby increasing the risk of fatigue. There are also unknowns, such as the presence of inclusions in the bolt material, which will act as stress raisers. In order to minimise the risk of fatigue failure, large end bolts should be replaced after about 15 000 running hours. This figure is determined from known fatigue information concerning the bolt material, the expected stress level applied and the operating speed of the engine. It is essential that large end bolts are replaced at the intervals suggested by the builder, even though they may not actually be showing signs of damage.

The Piston

Piston crowns can be visually inspected from above by lifting the cylinder head, but a thorough inspection requires the piston to be lifted. The connecting rod, or a section of it, will be lifted with the piston. The correct lifting tool must be used to avoid damage to the crown and, in the case of Vee type engines, to ensure that the piston is pulled cleanly up the cylinder bore. All threaded lifting holes in the piston crown should be cleaned before attaching the lifting tool. Routine piston lifting should take place at intervals of about 8000 hours to 15 000 hours, when piston ring packs are replaced. The gudgeon pin assembly should be checked for security and freedom but should not be dismantled until about 24 000 running hours have elapsed unless defects are detected at an earlier examination. With floating gudgeon pins the procedure should require no force, but a fitted pin will need to be driven out of the piston after the retaining clips have been removed. Gudgeon pin bearing surfaces should be checked for signs of wear or cracking, and the bores measured. The pin should be similarly checked and calibrated. As with other bearings, the acceptable clearance depends on the size of the engine, so the builder's information must be consulted before deciding on any replacement. All oil flow passageways in the connecting rod top end, gudgeon pin and piston should be checked clear using an air line, and inspected for signs of wear or cracking.

Piston Crown Inspection

With the piston out of the engine and laid on a safe clean surface, the crown must be inspected for signs of burning or cracking and any deposits removed. Tooling spaces must also be inspected and cleaned as necessary. Ring grooves need to be cleaned, and the axial clearance should be measured by pressing a new ring into the groove and inserting feeler gauges. The whole of the groove can be checked by rotating the ring to a new position. Acceptable clearances depend on the cylinder bore and vary between 0.0005 and 0.0015 of the bore. All ring grooves must be inspected for signs of damage, although it is the upper compression ring grooves which are most susceptible due to the high gas pressures and temperatures. If grooves are worn or damaged, the crown badly burned or the sides of the piston severely scored, the piston should be replaced and the damaged piston sent for reconditioning.

Ring Replacement

Complete sets of rings should be replaced at routine maintenance intervals. The new rings should be checked for signs of cracking and should be checked in the grooves to ensure they are the correct size. If the rings are of different types they must be placed in the correct order on the piston. The gap must be checked in an unworn part of the cylinder liner and the butts filed as necessary to give the correct minimum gap. Rings must be fitted on the piston using the ring expander provided by the engine builder, as this not only ensures safety for personnel but reduces stress in the rings during fitting. After fitting, all rings should be checked for freedom in their grooves and to ensure all parts can bottom correctly in the groove. When replacing a piston the rings should be guided into the bore of the liner using the guide provided to minimise the risk of jamming and subsequent ring/liner damage.

Cylinder Liner Inspection

The cylinder liner should be inspected when the piston has been removed. Any burning observed will be due to poor combustion and, if not serious, the liner can remain in service if the cause is rectified. If there are signs of cracking the liner should be replaced. Any ridges formed on the liner should be removed by grinding. Where an anti-polishing ring is fitted, it must be cleaned and checked to ensure it is fit for further service. The liner should be calibrated using an internal micrometer, and the readings recorded in fore and aft and port and starboard directions at a number of preset points down the liner. The liner should be replaced when it reaches the limit of wear. Maximum wear depends on the liner bore, but is usually about 0.004 times the bore. The amount of wear since the previous overhaul should be determined, as this allows the wear rate to be calculated. Liner wear rates should not exceed about 0.0075mm per 1000 hours running. The liner surface should be honed to remove the glaze, even if an anti-polishing ring is fitted. A light honing with stones of coarseness 80 to 400 should be used in accordance with the builder's instructions. The surface should be cleaned thoroughly after honing.

Lifting the Liner

The liner should only be lifted if it is to be replaced, the sealing rings are defective or the cooling surfaces require cleaning. Cooling surfaces can generally be checked through a plug in the cooling jacket, if the liner is of the jacketed type. Cooling bores can often be cleaned by flexible brushes. Care must be taken to ensure that any scale is removed before the liner is put back in service. The equipment provided should always be used when lifting and replacing cylinder liners. The liner should be calibrated in the cylinder block to check that no distortion has taken place during fitting. New O-ring seals should always be used when fitting cylinder liners.

The Cylinder Head

The cylinder head is lifted prior to piston removal and this gives the opportunity for a thorough overhaul, however, the fuel injector and relief valve can be removed without lifting the head. In some cases air inlet and exhaust valves are mounted in cages which can be removed and replaced without lifting the head, simplifying the overhaul of these components. Fuel injectors generally set the maximum running period between overhaul, which is at about 3000 hour intervals (see Table 3). Exhaust valves require attention at about 6000-10 000 hour intervals, but the piston may not require attention for double that period, and the cylinder head should only need to be lifted to gain access to the piston. The fitting of caged valves therefore reduces maintenance work. When a head lift is needed it should be removed as a complete unit containing all valves. These can be removed away from the engine.

Cylinder Head Maintenance

The head should be thoroughly cleaned and all parts dismantled. Cooling passageways should be inspected and descaled if necessary. Valves must be dismantled using the correct tools, and all parts cleaned and examined for signs of wear, corrosion, burning or other damage. Guide bushes should be removed from the cylinder head and the clearance between the valve stem and the guide checked. The bush must be replaced if clearance is excessive and gives cause for concern. Valve springs must be examined for signs of cracking or corrosion and the free length measured. If the length is less than that recommended by the manufacturer then the spring must be replaced. Valves must be reground to their seats, provided there is no sign of 'pocketing'. This is caused by excessive wear at the seat or excessive regrinding in the past, and causes the valve to be located too far into the seat. The consequent lower effective lift clear of the head reduces effective gas flow area. In such cases it is necessary to replace the seat insert, if the head is fitted with valve seat inserts. Otherwise the head should be replaced and the old one sent for reconditioning.

Caged Valves

Caged valves can be replaced by overhauled units and the units removed can be overhauled when convenient. The same conditions apply to the overhaul and replacement of parts, and care should be taken to ensure a good seal between the cage and the head when the cage is fitted.

Rotating Mechanisms

Where valves are fitted with rotating mechanisms, these should also be examined when the head/cage is dismantled. Any worn or damaged parts must be replaced. Effective operation of the rotocap unit depends on free movement of the spring loaded ball bearings (**Figure 34**). If the plate on which they sit is badly worn the amount of rotation will be reduced.

Clearance Checks

After the head has been refitted to the engine and at about 1000 hour intervals the clearance between each valve rocker arm and its mating valve stem must be checked and adjusted if necessary. This should be done while the engine is warm, unless the engine builder specifies otherwise. The clearance should be checked using feeler gauges and adjusted by means of the adjusting screw, generally located at the push rod end of the rocker. Clearance is required to allow thermal expansion of the valve during engine operation. As the exhaust valves are subject to higher temperatures than inlet valves, their rocker clearances are generally greater than for air inlet valves. Where multiple valves are employed there are two valve clearances to set, one for each valve, and the values may differ depending on the arrangement of the rocker mechanism (**see Figures 29 and 30**).

Water Test

Once the head has been mounted on the engine and all cooling pipes attached, a water test should be carried out to check for leaks. Air is bled from the system which is then subjected to full water pressure. The temperature should be that of a normally operating system.

The Fuel Injection System

The fuel injection system consists of a pump, high pressure pipe and an injector for each cylinder. Cleanliness is essential when dealing with any part of the fuel system. Frequent checks should be made for leaks during normal running of the engine, and the filters should be cleaned at 50 hour intervals.

Where residual fuel is burned in the engine, the fuel heater control must be monitored to ensure the correct viscosity is being achieved. If a fuel valve cooling system is fitted it must be checked to ensure sufficient fluid is circulating and that fuel valves are being maintained at the correct temperature.

Injectors

Fuel injection valves (injectors) should be removed from the engine and tested at about 3000 hour intervals, or more frequently if indicated by the engine builder. The lifting pressure of the valve should be determined in the test rig and recorded. The valve should then be dismantled and all parts cleaned. The lift of the needle valve and the spring should be checked for length while all parts are examined for cracks, scoring or other damage. All passageways, including those for coolant, should be blown through with air to check that they are clear. Nozzle holes should be checked for size and the nozzle should be replaced if wear is above the allowed limit. All protective coatings should be removed from any parts which are replaced. After the injector has been re-assembled, it should be tested in the test rig, preferably using a test fluid which has properties similar to the fuel which will be burned. Diesel oil can be used but test fluids also contain a lubricant and corrosion inhibitor. The injector should be adjusted to lift at the desired pressure and produce the correct spray pattern when it does lift. The needle valve should seat promptly when the pressure falls and there should be no sign of dribbling from the nozzle. The injector should hold a pressure close to the injection pressure. Coolant passageways should be blown through to check that they are clear and the injector wrapped in protective film and put away until required for use.

Safety

Safety is essential when testing injectors as high pressure fluids can cause injury. On no account should hands be placed in front of a spraying injector. Goggles and other protective clothing should be worn and the test rig should be fitted with an effective guard.

Fuel Pump Overhaul

If an engine operates on residual fuel, it can be advantageous to change to light fuel for about 5 minutes prior to stopping to remove and overhaul a fuel pump. Such overhauls are required at about 16 000 hour intervals. Pipes and the connection from the regulating shaft to the control rack must be disconnected before the fuel pump block can be removed from the engine. The pump cover is removed and the delivery valve extracted for inspection. If there is any sign of damage, the entire valve unit must be replaced. The plunger, body unit, rack assembly and tappet mechanism must be dismantled in accordance with the builder's instructions. Although helical control jerk type pumps are basically the same, their construction differs slightly from builder to builder and with critical devices like fuel pumps it is essential to follow the correct procedure to the letter. All parts should be washed in paraffin then laid out on a clean surface for inspection. Fine mating surfaces, such as the plunger and barrel or the sealing faces between the barrel and cover, should be inspected with a magnifying glass for signs of scratching or leakage. These surfaces must withstand very high pressure and any blemishes will soon lead to failure. If any blemishes are detected the parts should be replaced. Some manufacturers do not recommend shipboard overhaul of barrel and plunger assemblies; these should be sent ashore for attention.

Prior to Assembly

All parts should be cleaned again and coated with a thin oil prior to assembly. The plunger must be able to move in the barrel with the application of a light force. The plunger must also be able to rotate in the barrel, and the rack mechanism must be free to move. Where the tappet mechanism is spring loaded, the spring length should be checked prior to assembly of the unit. After fitting the pump to the engine it is necessary to connect and adjust the fuel rack linkage to give the correct fuel quantity at a particular control setting. This is discussed in 'Actuator Linkages' in Chapter 2.

Timing and Delivery Quantity Checks

A timing check and delivery quantity check should be carried out on an overhauled pump, or a pump in service if combustion problems indicate this to be necessary. If the engine operates on residual fuel this should be cleared out of the system prior to setting. The exact procedure for checking the timing and fuel delivery period differ with engine type but the following is typical.

Removal of plugs from the barrel body allows the plunger to be observed. With a light shining though one of the plug holes, the progress of the plunger top may be observed. The point at which it completely covers the spill port marks the beginning of fuel injection. Timing adjustment is covered in 'Injector Timing Adjustments' in Chapter 2.

The fuel delivery period may be checked by use of a calibration fluid. Although diesel oil can be used, it is generally considered better to use a calibration fluid which has a similar density to the fuel burned by the engine. The pump head is removed from the pump, the delivery valve taken out and then the head replaced. A fluid funnel is connected to the pump body so that fluid can gain access to the pump cylinder. The fuel rack is moved to its maximum delivery position and the engine turned so the pump plunger just covers the top of the spill port. The funnel is filled with fluid until fluid flows from the pump head. The level in the funnel should be maintained at the same level as the top of the pump head. The engine is turned and fluid will continue to flow out of the head, but the funnel level should be maintained by adding fluid to the funnel. When fluid ceases to issue from the head. it means a spill has occurred, which signals the end of injection. The crankshaft angle should be noted. All pumps can be checked in the same way and the end of injection angles compared. Deviations between all cylinders should not be more than 1°. Some methods allow the collection of fluid so that the actual delivery quantity can be checked.

Fuel Pipes

High pressure fuel pipes must be of the sheathed type if the engine room is to operate unmanned for any period of time, but they are advisable with any engine for safety reasons. The ends of the pipes must be correctly attached to the pump and the injector, and the drain from the space between the high pressure pipe and the sheathing must be clear. The alarm system which indicates a failed high pressure pipe should be checked after the pipe has been connected.

The Camshaft Drive System

The camshaft drive system should be inspected at about 10 000 hour intervals. If the drive is by means of chains, the pins, rollers and links should be inspected for signs of wear and cracking. Sprocket wheels should be inspected for damage and the alignment of the chain and sprockets checked using a straight edge. Chain stretch should be measured and if it exceeds the limit set by the manufacturer, the chain should be replaced. Tension of the chain on its sprockets should be adjusted to comply with the requirements of the manufacturer. If the camshaft drive is by means of gears the contact faces on all gears should be inspected for signs of cracking, scuffing or other damage. Slight damage may be corrected by honing. Any wheels which show significant damage must be replaced and the cause of the damage detected and corrected. Backlash in gear wheels can be checked by means of feeler gauges or a dial gauge. The acceptable backlash depends on the gear system, so manufacturer's data should be consulted. Whether chain or gear drive there should be adequate lubrication. The lubrication supply system should be operated to ensure oil is sprayed on the running parts.

Cam and Follower Roller Inspection

Inspection of cams and follower rollers should take place at about 4000 hour intervals. The lubrication supply should also be checked. Follower rollers should rotate freely on the cams. This can be checked by turning the engine slowly. Scuffing can occur if high impact forces exist between cams and followers and if the lubrication supply is defective. Individual cams or camshaft sections can be replaced if necessary (see Chapter 2, 'Camshaft, Cams and Valve Operating Systems').

Turbocharger System Cleaning

Turbocharger systems require cleaning periodically on both the air and gas sides. Charge air coolers should be cleaned on the air side at about 4000 hour intervals which can require the removal of the elements from the cooler casing. Deposits should be soft and easily removed, but care is needed to prevent damage to fins on the tubes. The cooler should be pressure tested following refitting to detect possible leaks from the water side. Where the water side is part of a fresh water circulation system it is unlikely that there will be any scale formation, but a check should be made while the cooler elements are removed.

Gas Side

Cleaning of the gas side of a turbocharger should be carried out at about 250 hour intervals. The actual interval depends on the quality of fuel being burned and should be adjusted in the light of experience. Dry cleaning methods are available, which employ ground walnut shells or similar and no speed reduction is needed when cleaning. Water washing is more common and requires the turbine speed to be reduced to half or less to prevent damage to the blades. If the engine drives an electrical generator it should be taken off-line prior to cleaning to prevent a load increase leading to a turbine speed increase. The casing drain is opened and water injected into the exhaust manifold just upstream of the turbine. In some cases an air supply is used to break the water jet into small particles. Water flow is restricted by an orifice in the supply line to prevent large quantities being injected. The flow out of the drain should be checked. Washing can be stopped when the water is clear. The turbine speed can be returned to normal over a 30 minute period and the drain closed.

Compressor Impeller

Cleaning the compressor impeller in service does not require any speed reduction. A measured quantity of water held in a container is forced into the eye of the impeller by air pressure from the impeller outlet. Water droplets run along the face of the impeller and remove the oily deposits from the impeller and volute casing. Cleaning effectiveness can be assessed from the air pressure rise across the compressor. If cleaning does not have the required effect it can be repeated.

Air Filters

Air filters should be cleaned at frequent intervals, determined by the cleanliness of the engine room atmosphere. Performance of the filter can be assessed by using a manometer across the filter. Filters are usually cleaned manually after removing them from the turbocharger.

Ball and Roller Bearings

Turbocharger bearings of the ball or roller type should be replaced at intervals of between 10 000 hours and 15 000 hours. Plain bearings have an indefinite life but must be inspected and have the clearance checked at about 8000 hour intervals. Thrust faces must also be checked. During any such overhaul the opportunity should be taken to manually clean the impeller and turbine and to inspect all parts.

Further Maintenance Considerations

Although the above describes a typical maintenance routine, the details are far from complete. The operating engineer should therefore make every effort to study the engine maintenance manual before attempting any overhaul, and should be aware of the problems which can exist in any maintenance procedure. Large engines may have external lubricating and cooling systems, but for smaller engines these are part of the engine, with coolers mounted at the side of the casing, with pumps driven by the crankshaft. These must also be examined and maintained. Instrumentation and control systems must be checked and defective items replaced immediately to ensure the engine is monitored effectively. Lubricating oil all lubricated systems should be sampled frequently and the samples sent to an approved laboratory for analysis. Only this can prevent the risk of engine damage from contaminated oil. Similarly, fuel should be sampled and analysed, which will not only avoid problems related to the supply of off-specification fuel, but will also reduce the risk of serious damage from the presence of catalytic fines and high sulphur levels.

Summary

Planned Maintenance: Engine builders provide schedules. These should be treated as guides and the operator must adjust times between overhauls in the light of experience.

Maintenance Periods: Engine loads and quality of fuel burned influence maintenance intervals.

Approved Spares: Only approved spares should be used which comply with the manufacturer's specification for quality.

Defective Components: Should be replaced as soon as possible as they can cause additional damage to the engine.

Surveys: Maintenance should be linked with survey requirements to avoid excessive work.

Hydraulic Tools: Must be kept in good condition and used as indicated to provide correct loadings and avoid injury.

Lifting Gear: All lifting equipment should have current test certificates.

Record Keeping: Should be part of good maintenance practice. Records should reflect work done and spares used.

Crankshaft Deflections: Taken in order to assess crankshaft alignment. Ensure the gauge is accurate and positioned at the correct location

Bearing Shells: Must be replaced as a set with correct 'nip' to ensure correct bore. Wear to be within limits set by manufacturer with no signs of corrosion on front or rear faces.

Journals and Pins: To be assessed for corrosion, cracking and other defects.

Large End Bolts: Must be replaced after a set operating period to minimise the risk of fatigue failure. Care must be taken to avoid overstressing and damage to bolts during maintenance.

Piston Rings: Check ring groove clearances and new rings prior to fitting.

Piston Crown Inspection: Checks to be made for crown burning, cracking: and other damage due to poor combustion or ineffective cooling.

Cylinder Liner Calibration: To be carried out to assess wear amount and wear rate. New liners must be checked after fitting.

Cylinder Head Valves: Must be overhauled to ensure they seat correctly. Seats and valves to be replaced as necessary. Rotation mechanism to be checked for functionality.

Caged Valves: Allow maintenance away from the engine and make for quicker overhaul.

Fuel Injectors: Must function without dribbling. Nozzles must be checked for atomisation and spray pattern.

Fuel Valve Cooling: Check cooling passageways are clear to ensure effective cooling.

Injectors: To be tested in approved rig and all safety precautions observed.

Sheathed Pipes: Must comply with rules if ship to operate UMS. Drain and alarm systems connected with such pipes must be checked for operation.

Fuel Pumps: Overhauled or sent ashore for service. Any parts showing signs of damage to be replaced. Test pump for timing and quantity after fitting.

Camshaft: Drive system to be checked for damage and alignment. Drive chains to be checked for stretch and tension. Lubrication system to be checked.

Cams and Followers: Check for scuffing and turning of roller on follower.

Turbocharger: In-service cleaning of compressor and turbine at intervals determined from experience. Bearings of roller or ball race type to be replaced at set intervals.

Index

A

Air cooler 76, 133
Air start valve 49
Air supply 101
Alarm system 85, 110
Aluminium Piston 26, 27
Aluminium piston skirt 23
Anti-dribble device (fuel pump) 60
Anti-polishing ring 38, 39
Articulated connecting rod 22
Atomisation 61
Automatic monitoring 106, 110

B

Balance weights 14
Bearing bolts 126
Bearing shell 'nip' 17, 125
Bi-metal bearing 15, 16, 125
Bore cooling 36, 37

C

Caged valves 45, 46, 129
Cams 50, 132
Camshaft 50, 52, 132
Camshaft drive system 51
Central cooling system 82
Chrome plated piston rings 32
Classification societies 110, 120
Cocktail shaker effect 26
Composite piston 24, 25
Compression ignition 1
Computer system 113
Connecting rod 17
    palm end 19
    split type 19
Constant pressure system 75, 76
Cooling system 81, 82
Cooling water 85
CP propeller 93
Crankcase explosion 84
Crankcase relief door 84
Crankshaft 13
    alignment 123
    deflections 123
Cylinder block 35
Cylinder cooling 34

Cylinder head 40, 128
Cylinder liner 34, 35, 103, 127
Cylinder liner stress 34
Cylinder power balance 105
Cylinder relief valve 48

D

Diagnostic system 112
Diesel electric 92

E

Electric governor 65
Emissions (NO_x) 62, 107
Engine control system 114
Engine fuel injection 53
Engine mounting system 96, 106
Engine selection 89
Engine systems 92
Exhaust gas recirculation 107, 108
Exhaust system 101
Exhaust valve 6, 41, 46, 129

F

Father and son engine system 92
Flexible mountings 98, 100
Fork and blade conn rod 20, 21
Four stroke cycle 4, 5
Fuel ignition delay 62
Fuel injection 53
Fuel injector 60, 63, 130
Fuel injector testing 130
Fuel injector timing 59, 105
Fuel pump 53, 55, 56, 105, 130
Fuel pump control 54, 106
Fuel pump plunger 55
Fuel pump timing 131
Fuel regulating shaft 71, 72

G

Governor actuator 66
Governor linkages 68, 70
Gudgeon pin 24, 25

H

Headroom 92
Helical control, fuel pump 54, 56

Index

Hydraulic jack 12, 121, 122
Hydraulic valve actuation 44, 45

I

Injector nozzle 61, 130
In-line engine 7, 8, 10, 11

J

Jacket water cooling 81

L

Large end bearing 19, 125
Layout diagram 89, 90
Lifting headroom 101
Load diagram 93, 94, 95
Lubrication 103
Lubrication system 81, 83

M

Monoblock construction 10
Multiple valves 41—43

N

Nodular cast iron 40
Non-metallic chocking 98, 99

O

Oil scraper ring 32
Overspeed trip 70, 72

P

Performance monitoring 113
Pilot fuel injection 62, 64
Piston cooling 24, 26
Piston crown 23, 24, 126
Piston ring clearance 30, 31
Piston ring materials 31
Piston rings 22, 30, 33, 127
Piston skirt 23, 24
Planned maintenance 118
Pulse system 75

R

Resilient mountings 98, 100

Rigid mountings 98
Rotating piston 26, 28, 29
Rotocap 47, 48
Running-in 103

S

Sensors 110
Sheathed fuel pipe 53, 132
Side-by-side conn rod 20, 21
Spare gear 122
Specific fuel consumption 89, 91
Speed governor 65
Spinners, valve stem 48, 49
Starting air system 49, 77, 80, 104
Supercharging 73

T

Thermal stress 36
Thin shell bearings 14, 16, 20, 125
Thrust bearing 17
Torsional vibration 15, 101, 125
Trend analysis 112, 122
Trunk piston engine 2, 3
Turbocharger bearing replacement 134
Turbocharger cleaning 133
Turbocharger rotor 76
Turbochargers 73, 133
Two stage fuel injection 62, 64
Two stroke cycle 5, 7, 73

U

UMS (Unmanned machinery space) 53
Underslung crankshaft 13, 124

V

Valve rotation 47, 48, 49
Variable fuel injection timing 57
Vee type engine 7, 8, 10, 20

W

Waste gate 77, 78
Water injection 108